REPORT OF THE PANEL ON FUTURE DIRECTIONS IN CONTROL THEORY: A MATHEMATICAL PERSPECTIVE

Wendell H. Fleming, Chairman

Supported by grant DMS-8617493 from the National Science Foundation with partial support from the Air Force Office of Scientific Research, the Army Research Office and by grant N00014-87-G-0100 from the Office of Naval Research.

Published by the
Society for Industrial and Applied Mathematics
Philadelphia
1988

Any opinions, findings, conclusions, or recommendations expressed in this report are those of the Panel and do not necessarily reflect the views of the funding agencies.

For additional copies write:

Society for Industrial and Applied Mathematics
1400 Architects Building
117 South 17th Street
Philadelphia, PA 19103

MEMBERS OF THE PANEL ON FUTURE DIRECTIONS
IN CONTROL THEORY

Wendell H. Fleming, Chairman,   Brown University

H.T. Banks	Brown University
G. Blankenship	University of Maryland
R. Brockett	Harvard University
J.A. Burns	Virginia Polytechnic Institute & SU
R.V. Kohn	New York University
A. Krener	University of California, Davis
A.J. Laub	University of California, Santa Barbara
J.L. Lions	College de France
S. Marcus	University of Texas
J.E. Marsden	University of California, Berkeley
S. Mitter	Massachusetts Institute of Technology
E. Polak	University of California, Berkeley
R.T. Rockafellar	University of Washington, Seattle
D. Russell	University of Wisconsin, Madison
E.D. Sontag	Rutgers University
G. Stein	Honeywell, Inc.

The Panel is deeply grateful to Andrzej Manitius of the National Science Foundation for his continual help and encouragement, and for his broad understanding of issues which needed to be addressed.

Preface

The Panel on Future Directions in Control Theory was formed in 1986. Its task was to assess the current status of research and to analyze future research directions in control theory viewed as a scientific discipline encompassing important research activities in mathematics, engineering, and other areas of science. In addition, the Panel addressed new challenges posed by modern science and technology, as well as opportunities presented as a result of revolutionary advances in computer technology and recent progress in related areas of mathematics. The present report summarizes the Panel's findings. The primary goal of the report is to assess the status and needs of this particular field. However, the Panel hopes that the report will also furnish some broader insights into the role that mathematics plays in modern technology.

We wish to thank Allyn Jackson for valuable help in recasting earlier drafts of the report in a style which we hope will prove more suitable for a wider audience. Thanks are due Anne Lynn Olinger for an excellent job in assembling and typing the manuscript.

The Panel wishes to acknowledge valuable suggestions and constructive criticisms from the following individuals, including members of the control community and some colleagues from other fields.

A. Arapostathis	R. Glowinski	L. Markus
Z. Artstein	J. Hammer	G. McFadden
J.P. Aubin	M. Hazewinkel	G. Meyer
J. Baillieul	U. Helmke	W.E. Miller
J. Ball	W. Helton	H. Nijmeijer
J. Baras	R. Hermann	L. Pandolfi
A. Bensoussan	H. Hermes	A. Perdon
V.E. Benes	G. Hewer	O. Pironneau
C. Berenstein	O. Hijab	S. Pliska
P. Bernhard	J.B. Hiriart-Urruty	M. Polis
J. Blum	L.R. Hunt	V.M. Popov
J. Brewer	M.Q. Jacobs	J.P. Quadrat
C. Byrnes	B. Jakubczyk	M. Robin
J. Chandra	F.C. Johnson	J. Schwartz
G. Chen	N. Kalouptsidis	S. Sethi
D. Claude	I. Karatzas	L. Tartar
P. Crouch	H.J.C. Kouts	R. Temam
J. Crowley	K. Kunisch	R. Triggiani
J. Demmel	H. Kushner	M. Verma
C. Desoer	J. Lagnese	J.T. Wen
D. Elliott	I. Lasiecka	D. Watanapongtse
R.J. Elliott	A. Leizarowitz	J. Willems
E. Emre	P.L. Lions	B. Wyman
A. Friedman	L. Ljung	G. Zames

Contents

CHAPTER 1. EXECUTIVE SUMMARY

In today's rapidly progressing science and technology, the field of control theory is at the forefront of the creative interplay of mathematics, engineering, and computer science. Drawing upon these disciplines, control theory brings powerful theoretical results to bear on advanced technologies. As a foundation of control systems engineering, it is at the heart of the new industrial revolution involving automation, computers, and robotics. Examples of its contributions are many. Control theory played a crucial role in the success of the Apollo project. More recently, control theory was an enabling science in the development of modern fly-by-wire aircraft such as the F-16 jet. Contemporary manufacturing is critically dependent on highly accurate process and machine control. Systems designed by making use of control theory are increasingly pervasive in our technological society: they are found in modern automobiles, climate control systems in large buildings, video cassette recorders, and commercial airplane autopilots.

The concept of control can be described as the process of influencing the behavior of a dynamical system so as to achieve a desired goal. Many physical systems are controlled by manipulation of their inputs based on the simultaneous observation of the outputs, in much the same way as an airplane is controlled by the pilot's actions based on instrument readings and visual observations. The control problem is to determine, on the basis of available data, the inputs necessary to achieve a given goal. The complexity of modern systems, inaccuracies in output measurements, and uncertainties about the system dynamics often make this problem extremely hard to solve. In modern automated systems the process of determining the inputs while observing the outputs takes place in control computers, microprocessors, or other electronic devices. The rules that govern the choice of appropriate control action are mathematical.

The need for control of systems and processes exists in many areas of human endeavor, from technology to medicine to economics. However, the laws of control for systems with complicated dynamics and measurement uncertainties are not well understood. Both basic and applied research is needed to make further progress possible. Basic research in control theory seeks to understand, in precise mathematical terms, the fundamental principles of control and the limitations on achievable results. This quest for fundamental understanding is in the spirit common to all basic sciences. Applied research in control theory is focused on the development of methods for analysis and design of advanced automatic control systems, including translation of control laws into computer control algorithms and software. Today's many smoothly functioning systems are the successful engineering implementations of mathematical principles of control theory, with modern computer technology being an enabling tool.

The present scientific and technological environment offers unprecedented challenges and opportunities for control. As methods developed recently have found their way into standard practice, they have opened the door to more complex applications. Recent mathematical advances and new computer technologies have greatly expanded the range of problems that can be solved. Above all, the current generation of applications poses new kinds of control problems. In many cases, new mathematical results and even fundamentally new approaches will be required.

These considerations demand that the United States maintain a strong research program in control, including fundamental mathematical research motivated by control applications. This Panel was convened to evaluate that endeavor. Its specific goals were to assess the current state of control theory from a mathematical perspective, to evaluate the needs of the control community, and to identify possible directions for future development.

Reflecting the diversity of the control community, the Panel's membership included university faculty from mathematics, applied mathematics, and engineering departments, as well as scientists affiliated with industrial and governmental organizations. The full Panel met twice, in November 1986 and May 1987. The Panel also wrote to over 150 members of the broadly based research community active in the mathematics of control, requesting their ideas and input. In preparing this report, it was decided to emphasize applications from engineering technology, since those are the best developed at present; there are, however, other kinds of applications, for example in economics or ecology, which have also seen activity and may well increase in importance. Within mathematics, the Panel interpreted the scope of control theory quite broadly, including fields which are linked to control applications through current research. Mathematical control theory is viewed not as an isolated mathematical discipline, but rather as an indispensable component of a technological partnership between mathematical theory, engineering practice, and hardware capabilities.

Based on the discussions during its two meetings and an analysis of the survey responses, the Panel arrived at a number of findings and recommendations. The following findings summarize our view of the present status of the field, including its distinguishing features and future trends.

Findings

The Panel found that control theory is a vibrant and expanding discipline. Nevertheless, control theory faces particular structural, educational, and communications challenges arising from its diverse origins and the wide applicability of its research. Control techniques are pervasive in a wide spectrum of applications of major scientific, technological, and economic importance. Present research activities in mathematical control theory show great vitality and diversity. There are well-developed ties to practical problems in engineering and current directions of research are strongly motivated by applications at the cutting edge of advanced technology. The distinctive characteristics of this field are summarized in the following findings.

- Control theory is an inherently interdisciplinary field. In addition to its ties with engineering, it has found applications in such diverse areas as financial economics, fishery resource management, prosthetic devices, and medicine, and it continues to expand its influence on other fields of science.

- Mathematics has historically played and will increasingly continue to play a critical role in the development of control science. The field has an excellent record of transfer of knowledge from mathematics to applications. Conversely, research motivated by control problems has had a fundamental impact on many areas of the mathematical sciences, often leading to development of deep and elegant theoretical results.

- The interplay between mathematics and engineering in the solution of control problems has proceeded in a leap-frog fashion. Advances in engineering create new theoretical problems which generate mathematical progress. That in turn provides a new understanding of engineering problems and leads to new engineering solutions. A characteristic feature of control science is that mathematical and engineering advances have been closely intertwined at every stage of development.

- The mathematics of control theory exhibits a wide variety of techniques that go beyond those associated with traditional applied mathematics. The tools of control theory are drawn from many branches of mathematics, such as ordinary, functional and partial differential equations, functional analysis, algebra, geometry, probability theory, discrete mathematics, numerical analysis, and computation. This richness may be ascribed to the fact that control research is driven by the diverse and changing needs of applications.

- Advances in the control field are made through a combination of mathematics, modeling, computation, and experimentation. A fundamental challenge in control modeling is to find parsimonious mathematical representations of complex physical phenomena, which are adequate for the analytical and computational needs of control design.

Looking toward the future, the Panel sees many challenges and opportunities. Further progress in advanced technologies, including such projects as the Space Station and the National Aerospace Plane, depend critically on the limits of performance of control systems. These limits may be extended by more accurate design based on sophisticated mathematical models and advanced scientific computing. Consequently, the Panel was led to the following findings.

- Many fundamental theoretical issues, such as control of nonlinear multivariable systems, or control of nonlinear partial differential equations, are not yet understood. Moreover, exciting new applications and technologies such as robotics, manufacturing, and space technology are providing a wealth of new control problems. Existing theories must be developed and expanded to meet these challenges.

- Experimental research in control theory is now becoming increasingly important. It has the dual purpose of finding the best control-oriented models of physical processes, and testing the validity of new control paradigms. The kinds of experimental data required in control are often very different from other sciences.

- Rapid advances in computing are having a significant impact on the control field. Theories developed a few years ago have resulted in standard tools for applications now commercially available in the form of computer codes. Dramatic increases in computing power allow researchers to explore problems which were totally impractical earlier. New computer architectures provide the possibility of real-time algorithms for identification and control. In addition, new computer technology offers unprecedented needs and opportunities for the development of new control paradigms.

Looking at the status of control theory, the Panel noted a major concern. If not addressed, there is a risk that the United States could lose its preeminence in this area of research. In particular, the Panel found:

- The continued health of control theory requires a steady flow of talented young mathematical scientists with a broad mathematical background and some training in applications. In the United States such young researchers do not seem to be entering the control field in sufficient numbers. There is a risk that the link between mathematics and control applications may become significantly diminished, greatly reducing the quality and the impact of the research.

Finally, looking at the perception of mathematical control theory in the broader science and engineering communities, the Panel observed the following.

- There is a misunderstanding by nonspecialists of the role that mathematical control theory plays in the development of new technologies. Very often, a computer chip (or other piece of hardware that implements a particular mathematical algorithm) is perceived as "the" scientific breakthrough, without understanding that the "brains" of this chip are in fact mathematical algorithms. For example, with respect to the Apollo mission, many suggest that an enabling technology was the on-board digital flight computer. It is often forgotten that the innovative mathematical algorithms stored in memory were equally responsible for the success of this mission.

Recommendations

Control problems will continue to provide a rich source of very complex mathematical problems. In addition to the payoffs through applications to modern technology, the solution of these problems will have impact on the development of mathematics itself. However, special efforts will be needed to ensure the continued development of control sciences in ways which take full advantage of present and future opportunities. The following recommendations are directed variously at the professional community, academic institutions and funding agencies. These recommendations are designed to enhance the impact of research in control theory on the development of technology and mathematical science within the United States.

To the professional community

- The control research community must always be on the lookout for new applications. Historically, the best work has been motivated by the needs of an important application, and this will continue to be the case.

- Control scientists should intensify their efforts in using advanced scientific computing. Large-scale computational modeling of both complex dynamical systems and various control principles will lead to new understanding of fundamental control issues. The next generation of problems is going to call for an integration of control methods with advanced computing concepts.

- There should be increased efforts to achieve greater unity of control theory. Exchanges of ideas between various groups within control fields should be encouraged, and they should involve graduate students and young researchers. Various centers, mathematical institutes, and summer schools are well suited to this task.

- The control research community should expand its interactions with other fields of mathematics, both pure and applied. Major conferences (such as those of AMS and SIAM) should be used to communicate to a broad mathematical audience questions that are important in control problems. Conversely, flow of ideas from other rapidly progressing fields of mathematics into control theory should be encouraged by various means, (including engineering conferences organized by IEEE, AIAA, IFAC, ASME, and AIChE).

To academic institutions

- Control science should be recognized as an interdisciplinary research activity involving creative interactions among mathematics, engineering and other sciences.

- Academic departments should establish an appropriate environment for conducting interdisciplinary research, including the development of evaluation criteria that recognize the unique features of multi-disciplinary research.

- Universities are encouraged to form special programs in control theory across department lines enabling students in areas such as mathematics and electrical and aerospace engineering to obtain the interdisciplinary training necessary for work on control and its applications. such programs depends on establishing a critical mass of faculty among the participating departments.

- The development of control theory should be assisted by the training of new PhD's in both mathematics and engineering. Those obtaining their PhD in mathematics departments should strive to master a broad spectrum of mathematical techniques characteristic of control theory and should also develop contacts with interested scientists in engineering, computer science or other science departments. Those obtaining their PhD in engineering departments should develop contacts with interested mathematicians, and should broaden their mathematical background in control theory significantly beyond the customary linear finite-dimensional system theory.

- Universities should assist in the provision of space, computational tools, and experimental facilities needed by researchers in control science. It is crucial that university administrations recognize the growing computational and experimental needs of mathematical research in control.

To funding agencies

- Special opportunities in control science call for the creation of new interdisciplinary research groups and centers. Several centers of moderate size would be better than a single large center, since each could then serve a somewhat different function. These centers would provide a way for experimentalists, control theorists, and mathematicians to work in close contact and collaboration. The students and postdoctoral fellows who emerge from a period of training at such a center will form the core of the next generation of control theorists nationwide.

- Mathematical and engineering aspects of control systems should be included as an integral part of new research initiatives in many areas of science and technology (e.g., robotics, space structures, computational mathematics, etc.). Due to the wide applicability of its paradigms, control theory is often an enabling science in the full development of these technologies.

- The current broadly-based research programs in mathematical control should be maintained and strengthened. It is impossible to forecast with assurance which fields will produce the most important advances, and it is unwise to try to do so.

- In addition to the usual areas of support, the agencies should enhance their support of the "experimental" side of control research. The term experimental is used here to denote both numerical and physical laboratory experiments of basic research type. The requirements for numerical experimentation range from dedicated CAD-type workstations to access to modern supercomputers. Funding of small-scale laboratory experiments on simple systems could provide tremendous opportunities for substantial improvements in control design.

- The exchange of ideas between engineers, mathematicians, and scientists should be encouraged. Highly interdisciplinary summer schools would provide an opportunity for engineers to be introduced to new mathematical tools, and for mathematicians to be introduced to new applications and computational tools. Increased international collaboration with leading institutes, such as INRIA in France, would provide a means for combining complementary skills of U.S. and foreign experts.

- Funding agencies should encourage and support the development of interdisciplinary educational programs combining mathematics, scientific computing, and engineering in the context of control. These programs should include numerical and laboratory experiments, focused on verification of mathematical theories of engineering systems, to demonstrate the usefulness and limitations of theoretical results and to illustrate the power of mathematical modeling.

CHAPTER 2. OVERVIEW

The nature of control theory

The science of control is concerned with modifying the behavior of dynamical systems to achieve desired goals. This broad definition covers a surprisingly diverse array of problems encountered in many areas of human endeavor. Control theory seeks to describe these problems in a quantitative way, focusing on those that lend themselves to a precise mathematical description. Control theory has two objectives: to understand the fundamental principles of control, and to characterize them mathematically in a way that can ultimately be used to compute *control inputs* to the system, or to design automatic control systems. Increasingly, the science of control is required to deal with not a single dynamical system, but a complex interconnection of dynamical systems, in the presence of uncertainties on the *observed outputs* and on the dynamics of systems themselves.

The subject has several historical origins, with two related but different sets of ideas that form the central themes of the field.

The first central theme is concerned with the idea of *feedback*, a control scheme in which the inputs to the system are determined on the basis of the concurrent observations of the outputs. Both inputs and outputs are evolving in time. Key to the idea of feedback is a real-time comparison of available outputs with their desired values to obtain a measure of error. This measure is then used to determine inputs that will subsequently decrease the error. The resulting chain of cause-and-effect relations—input,dynamics, output, measurement, comparison, error, input—forms a loop, thereby creating a new dynamical system which contains the original one inside it. The key questions that arise in this context are the stability and the dynamic behavior of the new *"closed-loop"* system. This simple description hides a great complexity of modern feedback schemes that employ hundreds of variables fed at great speed to control computers. The concept of feedback contains a rich variety of mathematical themes that have their historical roots in the Lyapunov stability theory and the Nyquist complex variable method. It continues to lead to new, intriguing research questions while the technology furnishes new means for implementing feedback schemes. The "fly-by-wire" F-16 jet described later in this chapter is a pinnacle of technological achievement of the feedback concept.

The second central theme is concerned with the idea of optimal control. In this context, the goal of control is formulated as the minimization (or maximization) of a performance index, a mathematical quantity that characterizes the difference between the desired and the actual system's behavior over a period of time. One seeks a control as a function of time minimizing the performance index. Solving this problem results in a preprogramming of the control input for the entire period. This is often referred to as the trajectory optimization problem. Mathematically, the roots of this theme belong to the calculus of variations. A related idea is the optimization of the shape of geometric objects and, more generally, the optimal design of structures. Control theory has revitalized and reformed the calculus of variations by bringing in new ideas of switching and rapidly oscillating control functions. It also led to contemporary nonsmooth analysis, and to new computational techniques for trajectory optimization. The space shuttle ascent trajectory was computed by using these techniques in three-dimensional space and represents an outstanding example of a successful high-tech application linked to this theme.

The two themes are intertwined in several ways. One of the fundamental statements of control theory is that under certain conditions an optimal control problem can be solved by constructing a feedback. Conversely, in certain cases a given feedback system has a corresponding optimal control problem for which the given feedback is the solution. In linear theory, one can design a feedback system by using an algebraic matrix equation, to solve a variational problem. This method leads to elegant and robust numerical algorithms. Other problems arising in control theory are solved by methods that draw upon these two themes in various combinations.

The fundamental reason for using feedback is to accomplish performance objectives in the presence of uncertainty. In many situations the knowledge of the system is only partial, or the available model is based on many simplifying assumptions that make it inaccurate. The system may be subject to external disturbances, such as air turbulence around an aircraft. In addition, the output measurements are often corrupted by noise. An effective feedback reduces the effects of uncertainties, because it tends to compensate for all errors, regardless of their origin.

The term feedback covers a wide spectrum of concepts, including complicated multi-loop, nonlinear, and adaptive feedbacks in today's systems, as well as the "intelligent" feedbacks of the future. In a broader context, feedback can be a way to describe and understand circular interactions taking place in complex physical systems. In fact, current research on nonlinear dynamical systems often deals with complicated interactions which can be interpreted as internal feedbacks. Living organisms and computer algorithms also have internal feedback loops. The goal of understanding feedback dynamics therefore transcends the boundaries of control theory.

Controlling a dynamical system involves several fundamental processes:

- *modeling* of the system based on physical laws;

- *system identification* based on experimental data;

- *signal processing* of the output by filtering, prediction, state estimation, etc;

- *synthesizing the control input* and applying it to the system (active control).

The *modeling* issue in control is different from its counterparts in other areas of science, despite evident similarities. This issue is discussed more extensively in a subsequent section.

System identification may be defined as the process of determining a model of a dynamical system using observed input and output data. In the event that the model is given and only its parameters are unknown, system identification reduces to parameter estimation. An integral and important part of control theory, identification is related to the area of inverse problems in applied mathematics. Performing system identification often requires experimentation to generate input signals and record the outputs. A variety of statistical and computational techniques are often used to process the data and obtain the model. Present research work in the area of identification focuses on fundamental questions such as solvability and well- posedness of identification problems, and on parameter estimation methods for various classes of models.

Signal processing exists independently of control theory. However, there is a substantial overlap between the two fields, and the contributions from the control community to signal processing have been highly significant, particularly in the area of filtering and smoothing. These terms refer to the reconstruction of signals from observations corrupted by noise. Applications include communications, tracking of data from satellites, speech processing, and image reconstruction. The pictures of outer planets sent back by the Mariner and Pioneer space probes would be almost useless without this computerized image reconstruction capability.

Synthesizing the control is dependent on the model, identification, and signal processing, as well as on the goal of control and the approach taken. Complications of these processes give rise to various current research topics of control that generate a great deal of interest:

- *Robust control* theory aims at finding a feedback which guarantees a significant independence of closed-loop system features from model and signal uncertainties. For example, a robust feedback may be expected to stabilize not only the system for which it was designed, but a whole parametrized family of systems.

- *Adaptive control* is concerned with the automatic adjustment of control laws during the control process. Systems that change with time or are not initially well known are the main applications of adaptive control. An adaptive feedback law often performs a self-adjustment based on an automatic system identification.

- *Multivariable control* is an approach to systems with many inputs and outputs that are cross-coupled. The goal of feedback may then include an additional task of decoupling in order to achieve a noninteracting control.

- *Nonlinear control* theory is concerned with fundamental questions arising in the control of inherently nonlinear dynamical systems. Many current research efforts in this area focus on geometric methods.

- *Stochastic control* applies to situations in which the system or its perturbations can be modeled in a probabilistic setting. Filtering and prediction of random output signals are natural ingredients of stochastic control.

- *Distributed parameter control* deals with situations in which the spatial distribution of variables inside the system is critical to the goals of control. Examples include control of vibrations in elastic plates and beams, control of heat transfer, control of systems having internal delays, and control of fluid flow systems.

Several other topics of control theory are becoming increasingly important due to the continuing progress in computer technology. These include *learning* and *self-organizing* systems, *hierarchical control* systems, *intelligent control*, and *discrete-event control* systems.

The role of mathematics

In control theory, mathematics plays a dual role. First, the control problems have to be formulated in precise mathematical terms that reflect the underlying physical context. In this process, a crucial step often requiring creative vision is the identification of the appropriate mathematical structure. This structure must be at once rich enough to describe the problem adequately, and simple enough to be mathematically tractable. The identification of such a structure is difficult, because it requires knowledge of both the physical problem and the areas of mathematics that may offer novel formulations. The second role of mathematics is to bring the power of mathematical machinery to bear on the solution of control problems once they have been precisely formulated. At this point, deep mathematical questions are frequently encountered, and answering them usually requires new mathematics.

The fundamental reason why such deep questions arise is that control problems are different from those encountered in other areas of mathematics. For example, while classical formulations of problems in ordinary and partial differential equations involve questions concerning the solutions of equations, the control-theoretic formulations are concerned with modifying the equations in order to obtain solutions with desired properties. Furthermore, there is no a priori reason why a control input should be a continuous function of time, or why nonlinearities in a control system should be smooth. Therefore, most of the established mathematical results which rely on various continuity and regularity hypotheses simply do not apply to control problems. Solving these problems under new, more general assumptions often leads to new mathematical results.

A striking feature of control theory is the broad range of mathematical tools that are employed. They include complex function theory, linear and abstract algebra, ordinary and partial differential equations, variational methods, stochastic processes, functional analysis, operator theory, differential geometry, Lie algebras, algebraic geometry, discrete mathematics, optimization, and numerical analysis. The vignettes in Chapter 4 give an idea of the role that these tools play in various problems of control theory. This role is often very different from that seen in traditional applied mathematics. In fact, control theory has established many unexpected direct connections between pure mathematics and engineering.

In developing new mathematical results and connections, control theory has not only contributed to the solution of applied problems, but has also made an impact on mathematics itself. Examples illustrating this point are given in the vignettes in Chapter 4. The following brief list will serve as a guide:

- variational problems: work on extensions of Pontryagin's maximum principle has led to many abstract and beautiful variational principles that are now becoming increasingly useful in other mathematical research.

- linear systems: work on the matrix Riccati equation, the geometric theory of linear multivariable systems, and other related topics has had a large impact on two-point boundary value problems, linear algebra, and operator theory. It has also begun to influence research in numerical linear algebra.

- non-smooth analysis: originally developed in connection with non-smooth optimal control problems, this area has now become an increasingly important source of new tools in analysis and in mathematical programming. For example, new results on periodic solutions of Hamiltonian systems have been obtained by using this approach.

- control of partial differential equations: questions of boundary control and exact controllability of hyperbolic systems has led to new results on the regularity of solutions under weak hypotheses. These results probably would not have arisen in a traditional context.

- stochastic control: in the theory of viscosity solutions for first and second order nonlinear partial differential equations, optimal stochastic control representations of solutions has played an important role. Stochastic control has also made an impact on large deviation theory for Markov stochastic processes.

- robust control: new formulations involving the (Hardy) H-infinity space have led to interesting new questions and developments in operator theory and in complex function theory.

- nonlinear control: the study of controllability has led to new results on the integrability of singular distributions on manifolds. In another context, a rich interplay between the system Lie bracket structure and variational problems was discovered.

The issues of modeling in control theory

The choice of a mathematical model for a given system is obviously crucial for the control of the system. A special difficulty arises, however, when for inherent reasons the system is imperfectly known. It may not be possible to write down the exact dynamic laws, or, even if this can be done, the resulting equations may be so complex that a control design based on them would be impossible. Fortunately, the use of "imperfect" mathematical models does not have to be a total impediment. A valuable lesson that has been learned, and which cannot be overemphasized, is that complicated systems can be controlled by feedback on the basis of quite simple models. Thus the modeling issue in control can sometimes be very different from the one in physics, despite many similarities. In control theory, the issue centers on finding robust, mathematically parsimonious models that may be constructed from available data by a process of system identification. Questions of adequate parametrization, identifiability, and invariance of representation with respect to groups of transformations take on considerable importance.

It is extremely important to recognize that many of the most successful applications of control theory could not have been possible without the ability to use simple mathematical models in the control design. On the one hand, this feature has been the "saving grace" of the field—it has made control practical. On the other hand, it has led to much controversy within the field about the relevance of various mathematical approaches to control, and has caused scientists from other areas to misunderstand the nature of research in control. Within the field, the differences of opinion about the relevance of various approaches can be traced back to the existence of two basic trains of thought. In their extremes, they can be described as follows.

One extreme viewpoint holds that model imperfections are not really relevant in the context of control, because feedback reduces the effect of uncertainty, including modeling errors. Therefore, accurate models are not needed for control. What is needed instead is a powerful feedback design methodology that would yield a robust, adaptive, fault-tolerant control system. The emphasis is thus placed on the controller, at the expense of the model. This viewpoint underlies many advanced theories on the design of controllers for a generic class of models, and may lead to a belief that the control theory does not need to deal with sophisticated models, such as for example, partial differential equations. Thus, some control experts feel that "a more robust control theory is needed, not better models."

The other extreme view places great emphasis on the use of an accurate model derived from physical laws, while the control design is assumed to be easy or at least computationally feasible once the model is firmly established. The emphasis on the model makes this approach accessible and appealing to other scientists, such as physicists and fluid dynamicists. The assumption that the model is accurate also is used to justify many abstract mathematical investigations of control laws based on such models. In its extreme form, this viewpoint ignores the whole problem of model uncertainty and its impact on control design. It may lead one to believe that the only way to design a control system is to have first a very accurate microscopic model, a belief which represents a fundamental misunderstanding of the nature of control research.

In fact, adherence to either extreme viewpoint without regard for the other is unhealthy. The control community must recognize that the successful treatment of new applications depends on the development of new models and new theories for those models, and, concurrently, on continued progress in feedback design techniques. Although the dichotomy presented above is intrinsic to the field and will always be present in some measure, significant breakthroughs are most likely to come from research that combines the best of both approaches. In a particular application, one or the other viewpoint may be more realistic: in process control, for example, robust controller designs based on simple linear models are most often the answer, whereas for customized designs in advanced aerospace applications model accuracy may well be critical.

Another feature of the subject which often produces confusion is the absence of a "canonical" model to be controlled. There is no analogue, for example, of the Navier-Stokes equation in fluid dynamics. Even within a particular area of application, the models customarily used for simulations may not be adequate for control. Issues which are absent or relatively minor for simulation—such as the number of actuators or sensors and their locations, or the limitations of real-time computation—may be crucially important to the control of a system. The diversity of models used by control theory is one of its strengths, lending the subject breadth and variety.

Experimentation is becoming increasingly important. Perhaps the two primary goals of experimentation for control are model development or validation, and simulation of the closed-loop performance. It is important to emphasize that models suitable for open-loop simulation may not be appropriate for control studies. Therefore, the type of experiment needed by the control theorist can differ from the "standard" experiment. An obstacle here is the magnitude of some of the systems whose control is proposed, or the costliness of mistakes, as in the case of a space station or nuclear power plant. Actual applications often allow no room for experimentation of the kind that could lead to genuine mathematical insight. Opportunities for small-scale experiments designed to test ideas on simple systems can be therefore of great benefit to theoretical progress.

Historical development of the mathematics of modern control theory

The early period

Although the origins of control theory can be traced back at least into the last century, the subject is relatively young as an identifiable branch of applied mathematics. Early work included Maxwell's analysis of system stability of steam engines with governors in 1868 and Minorsky's work on ship steering in the 1920's. The classical results of Nyquist, Bode, and others in the context of single-loop feedback amplifiers showed that feedback control can guarantee satisfactory performance even in the face of quite poor knowledge of the system.

In the 1940's and 1950's, Norbert Wiener made seminal contributions to control theory. His ideas about "cybernetics" provided a framework in which problems o control and communication could be considered in a unified manner. Wiener also developed a method for the filtering, prediction, and smoothing of signals in the presence of noise. Subsequent development made essential use of the then-emerging subject of stationary stochastic processes and led eventually to the Bode-Shannon concept of information.

The milestones

An important thread in the development of control theory started after World War II with Wald's sequential analysis and Bellman's dynamic programming. These theories were motivated by problems of optimal statistical decision-making and of sequential planning or resource allocation. Their conceptual contribution was to consider a family of dynamic optimization problems, parameterized by their initial states. The centerpiece was the dynamic programming equation for optimal performance, from the solution of which an optimal feedback control law could be determined. Work in linear and nonlinear programming, another area of optimization that began in the same period, emphasized inequality constraints, which had until then largely been neglected. Researchers in this area took a lead in devising computer-oriented numerical methods, an approach that subsequently became very important in control.

Soviet engineers in the 1950's expressed an interest in optimal transients in which nonlinearities, saturation effects, and bounds on the control could not be ignored. Conversations between these engineers and mathematicians at the Steklov Institute in Moscow led to Pontryagin's discovery of the "maximum principle" for optimal trajectories of a system. The maximum principle opened the way to a systematic study of optimal trajectories with discontinuous control functions in the presence of constraints on both the state and the control. This in turn brought out deep connections with the calculus of variations, and stimulated further theoretical studies in more abstract optimization problems that have significant interaction with nonlinear functional analysis. Perhaps the most significant contribution of this theory was the impetus it gave in the 1960's to a large research effort on numerical methods for trajectory optimization. This research ultimately led to successful designs of trajectories for many space missions, including the Apollo program and the space shuttle flights.

Another milestone of control theory in the late 1950's was the discovery of the Kalman (or Kalman-Bucy) filter. The earlier Wiener theory of filter design was limited by assumptions such as the stationarity of the random process, and required solving an integral equation or factoring a Fourier transform. Kalman's filter was free of these inconveniences, and could be implemented as a sequential algorithm on a small computer. Its design depended on solving a now-celebrated matrix Riccati equation. By a duality principle, a linear feedback controller was shown to be described by equations of the same type. These ideas have had great impact worldwide and have stimulated a great deal of research on feedback control and filtering, leading to many applications of control theory. An algorithm based on the Kalman filter was implemented in an on-board computer of the Apollo spacecraft, and used for trajectory corrections in space missions.

The period of diversification: late sixties and seventies

These successes of control theory attracted many new participants, including mathematicians fascinated by the associated research opportunities. As new tools were introduced, the theory widened and became diverse, to the extent that a "Tower of Babel" phenomenon has arisen: specialists in one branch may experience difficulties in understanding the work of experts in another. However, to this day the linear-quadratic regulator theory postulated by Kalman plays the role of a universal language accessible to all branches.

Linear system theory has been very vigorous during the last 25 years. With the introduction of the concepts of controllability, observability, canonical forms, state-space realization, and the linear-quadratic-Gaussian regulator problem, this area has become a conceptual foundation for the development of the field as a whole. It served as a model for generalizations to nonlinear and distributed parameter systems, and a testing ground for all new paradigms of control. At the same time, it has continued its own development, offering a wealth of new concepts, precise results, and algorithms. The geometric approach to linear systems has led to the important concepts of supremal invariant and controllability subspaces, disturbance decoupling, non-interacting control, and elegant asymptotic analysis of high gain feedback systems. Related to these ideas was important work on the numerical analysis of linear control problems, which made connections with ongoing research in numerical linear algebra. In recent years, many algorithms of advanced linear control theory have been incorporated in various commercial software packages, including those for personal computers.

Work on the feedback control of systems governed by nonlinear ordinary differential equations has introduced methods from differential geometry, Lie algebras, and nonlinear dynamics. The results on feedback linearization and nonlinear decoupling which led to the Frobenius I control system described later in this report were among the successes of this approach. These techniques also have led to many elegant results on controllability. Recent adaptations of methods from nonlinear dynamics have extended feedback stabilization capabilities to classes of nonlinear systems which are not feedback linearizable.

In the late sixties and early seventies progress was made in extending the linear-quadratic theory to infinite-dimensional systems, i.e., systems governed by partial differential equations, functional differential equations, integro-differential equations, and general differential equations in Banach spaces. This work proceeded on several tracks: some investigators tried to obtain general operator-type formulations applicable to broad classes of infinite-dimensional systems, while others began with specific equations such as the wave equation or a delay-differential equation, gaining intuition from the structure of the problem before proceeding to more general formulations.

Progress made over a period of time, under the strong influence of the French school, has made it clear that there is no general formula encompassing all infinite-dimensional systems. Rather, each case raises its own highly technical questions which lead to delicate studies of the regularity of solutions, the validity of various finite-dimensional approximation schemes, variational formulations, homogenization, etc. Current challenges include the treatment of systems governed by linear partial differential equations or relatively simple delay equations which allow the observations and controls only at the boundary of the spatial domain. Understanding the control problem for nonlinear infinite-dimensional systems will evidently require major conceptual breakthroughs.

Another link with partial differential equations is provided by the optimality equation derived by the method of dynamic programming in continuous time and space variables. This equation, now called the Hamilton-Jacobi-Bellman equation, has been a source of inspiration for some leading analysts, who have recently invented the notion of "viscosity solution." If such new analytical methods ultimately lead to methods for solving the Hamilton-Jacobi-Bellman equation in new contexts, they could provide an additional tool for the design of nonlinear feedback controls.

Convex analysis has provided fresh approaches to control theory and the calculus of variations, as well as a bridge to mathematical programming and numerical methods in operations research. Convex analysis widened in the early seventies into "nonsmooth analysis," a new setting which has provided results on long unsolved optimal control problems. The theory of variational inequalities, which was developed in the 1960's, has served in the study of free boundary problems and optimal stopping. In motivating the development of such new analytical tools, control theory has demonstrated the potential to contribute to basic mathematics as well as to its own goals.

The field of probability has provided the theory of stochastic control and filtering. Work on nonlinear filtering has continued to extend the Kalman filter, and to inject many new ideas. The problem has never been solved in full generality and continues to present a challenge. Stochastic versions of optimal control problems generated much interest among mathematicians in the 1970's and 1980's. This area is among the most active and has connections to asymptotic analysis for the celebrated exit problem for stochastic processes. On the side of applications, the conceptual framework of stochastic control theory has begun to play an important role in the control of large interconnected power systems and in stock portfolio management.

Algebra has contributed in significant ways to the development of a more powerful linear system theory. The introduction of the terminology of rings and modules has led to elegant reformulations of earlier results on controllability and observability and has given rise to many generalizations that have played an important conceptual role. Computational algebraic methods such as factorization over polynomial rings are now becoming important. Algebraic geometry methods have led to significant contributions to the Nyquist stability criterion for multivariable systems, and to the solution of the "parametrization problem" in system identification.

The eighties: robust control, connections to computer science

In the late 1970's and early 1980's, the design of feedback control underwent a deep revision. After many years in which state-space methods based on differential equations prevailed, design based on input-output or frequency domain analysis has made a comeback. This approach appears well suited to the study of robust controls, since it permits the parameterization of all stabilizing controllers and the selection of one whose behavior is uniformly desirable over all frequencies. Mathematically, the H^∞ approach to robust control has made use of interpolation theorems and complex function theory [the so-called H^∞ space]. Its mathematical depth and practical importance place this theory among the success stories of the eighties.

Connections with computer science have started playing a more important role with the development of artificial intelligence and the introduction of new computer architectures. Recently, expert systems designed to automate the theoretical and numerical solutions of optimal stochastic and filtering problems have been introduced. Work on the integration of symbolic and numerical computation in the context of control is in progress. The concept of intelligent control is currently under development. Among its goals are to achieve a blend of present-day control theory with the problematic of artificial intelligence. Discrete-event system theory provides a link to the theory of extended state machines, and may in the future provide a modeling tool for the evaluation of computing systems' performance.

Mathematical control theory remains a vigorous and diverse research activity in the 1980's. In addition to work in established directions such as those mentioned above, the theory is expanding to encompass other kinds of applications. New paradigms are being sought for new classes of problems, such as those whose dynamics are best described in terms of discrete events. In these and other ways, mathematical control theory continues to be driven by a broad range of current applications.

Contemporary applications of control theory

This section presents some of the exciting contemporary applications exemplifying the use of modern mathematical techniques in control systems, and provides a background on the increasing breadth of applications.

The established methods of control theory have had a pervasive impact on modern technology. Single-loop control systems based on classical principles and, more recently, the first generation of adaptive controllers, can be found in many industries. These systems also surround us in everyday life. Examples of the wide spectrum of such applications are given later in this section. This wide applicability of control systems is due not only to modern instrumentation (sensors, actuators) and inexpensive electronic hardware, but also to the ability of control theory to handle dynamical systems in spite of uncertainties in the model and the output signals.

While applications of well-established methods are growing at an increasing rate, the practical uses of advanced theoretical concepts are still concentrated primarily in high technology applications such as aerospace. This situation is about to change due to dramatic progress in computer technology, and to increased industrial competition worldwide. New computer technology offers the means to implement more sophisticated control algorithms, while the need to maintain a competitive industrial position provides the incentives to achieve increased precision, efficiency, and reliability of control. The increasing number of engineers with strong mathematical background is another factor contributing to this change. In this context, it is encouraging to note that in the 1980's both academic and industrial sectors are pursuing more research themes in common than in earlier eras, thus facilitating the flow of new ideas.

There is naturally a certain delay between a development of new theoretical ideas and their use in control applications. In some cases, today's applications implement theoretical ideas invented one or two decades earlier. But it is also true that rather new mathematical techniques have already seen significant applications. The following items illustrate both types of applications.

- The Space Shuttle is equipped with a sophisticated control system that includes two different digital autopilots, one to handle ascent to and descent from orbit, and another one to handle the Shuttle maneuvers and payload deployment on orbit. The control and data processing functions are performed by five identical IBM AP-101 computers, each with 104K of 35-bit word memory. The control laws of the orbit flight control system implement various modern control principles, such as state estimation and bang-bang control. For example, the reaction control system includes preprogrammed switching curves in the phase plane of each axis rotation which serve to generate negative and positive firing commands for thrusters. The design required extensive studies of possible adverse dynamic interactions between spacecraft and flexible payloads. As a precaution, restrictions on control law parameters such as angular rate limit, pulse size, etc. were implemented. In addition to these systems, there is also an innovative experimental autopilot, which contains a three-dimensional phase space control law combined with a linear programming algorithm performing the jet selection. Flight tests of this autopilot showed its very good adaptability to vehicle configuration changes. Finally, the expected upgrade of AP-101 to 256K memory and faster processing rate will pave the way to the use of even more advanced control concepts. Planned operational increments in software for 1989 include an optimal control algorithm to improve fuel economy of axis rotation maneuvers, and an on-board calculation of composite orbiter/remote manipulator/payload mass properties. Shuttle orbit control experience will benefit the development of the Space Station.

- A new therapy for the treatment of certain cerebral edemas or malignant brain tumors is based on the simultaneous administration of vasopressin and cortisone. Due to the highly nonlinear character of the body's system regulating the secretion of these hormones, the relative rates at which they are introduced are critical. Two French researchers cast this as a 2x2 nonlinear multivariable control problem, and applied a nonlinear decoupling-feedback linearization method based on a Lie algebraic approach. Their work was recognized by a Seymour Cray Award in 1986. The treatment is now routinely used in the neurosurgery clinic of the Hôspital de la Pitie in Paris.

- While many advances in control arise from research toward a recognized need, others emerge as unexpected benefits from theoretical advances. An example of the latter pattern is offered by the Frobenius I helicopter autopilot control system recently developed at NASA's Ames laboratory. The dynamics of helicopter flight is governed by twelve nonlinear ordinary differential equations. Early work at NASA Ames led researchers to ponder methods for controlling nonlinear systems by using feedback to put the system in a triangular form. Linearization methods analogous to Poincare's "resonance condition," but incorporating feedback in a crucial way, were suggested. In the early 1980's, mathematicians working in geometric control theory established necessary and sufficient conditions for the existence of a nonlinear feedback which yields a closed-loop system diffeomorphic to a linear, controllable system in Brunovsky canonical form. Discussions between some of these mathematicians and members of the NASA Ames research staff led to the realization that the helicopter system satisfies the conditions for feedback linearization to sufficient accuracy, and hence could be controlled by a suitable nonlinear feedback law. The resulting control system was recently tested in real flight conditions with successful results.

- The production of electricity is influenced by unpredictable phenomena, which can be modeled stochastically. Among these phenomena are uncertainties in demand and possible breakdown of power plants. In the case of hydroelectric power generation, the amount of water available depends on fluctuations in rainfall. Studies of the management of energy production systems using stochastic control methods were undertaken in France at the National Institute for Research in Computer Science and Automation (INRIA). A particular study focused on a relatively simple system in New Caledonia, consisting of eight thermal power plants and a dam. The goal was to choose, as a feedback control, a feasible production schedule which met the demand at the least possible expected cost. Model identification involved estimating the drift and diffusion coefficients in a stochastic differential equation. Optimal feedback controls were found by numerical solution of the partial differential equations and inequalities of dynamic programming. For large power systems, the high dimensionality of the problem is a barrier. However, this study had an important influence on the conceptual framework with which engineers approach electrical power generation control problems. In particular it led to wider acceptance of the stochastic control paradigm by engineers in Electricité de France.

- The most critical component of many of today's lightweight and highly maneuverable aircraft is their digital flight control systems. In modern designs, including the F-16 and the experimental forward swept wing X-29, mechanical linkages are replaced by digital computers and electrical wires (so-called "fly-by-wire systems"). In order to enhance maneuverability, these aircraft are also designed to be statically (i.e., open-loop) unstable. Lighter than conventional mechanical systems, digital fly-by-wire control systems, can be programmed to change the aircraft's flight characteristics. The control system operates full-time to stabilize the aircraft and to support various decision aids for the pilot. This design is made possible by the use of digital control systems which are *fast enough* to respond to aerodynamic fluctuations and actively stabilize an unstable dynamical system. The application of control theory to the design of these aircraft is truly a tremendous achievement. It is clear that future "super-maneuverable" aircraft will be possible only if continued progress is made in fast, robust controller designs. Problems similar to those described above also occur in flutter suppression devices and active controllers designed to improve ride quality in commercial aircraft.

- The 10-meter telescope for the Keck observatory on Mauna Kea in Hawaii (under construction) has a mirror composed of 36 hexagonal segments that can be individually moved by actuators. Those are in turn controlled by a computer that attempts to focus the picture by using a feedback algorithm. The whole frame of the telescope consists of many interconnected beams, that exhibit vibrations caused by winds. The controller must maintain good focus of the image in spite of joint, frame, and mirror vibrations. The control system was designed by using a high-dimensional finite element approximation of the structure dynamics that captured the most significant vibration modes. Extrapolation of this control technique to other large, deformable mirrors that would contain hundreds, or even thousands of tiles is being considered, but there may be a computational barrier to simultaneous control of that many signals.

- Active control of structures is spreading to the construction industry. In the design of some of the tallest buildings, active damping systems are being considered. Theoretical studies done by structural engineers indicate that a properly designed, active-controlled tuned mass damper system can reduce building dynamic motion caused by high winds. Some systems of powered, passive tuned, mass dampers have been installed on the Citicorp Center building in New York and on the John Hancock Tower in Boston, but they do not use full active damping. Other potential uses of control in structural engineering involve active tendon control, where an electronic control system acts through a hydraulic actuator on tendons (cables) to tighten or release them in a timed manner so as to counteract the dynamic building response.

The impact of established control concepts of contemporary industry is so pervasive that it cannot be described in a short space. The following two items exemplify this impact:

- One of the main application fields for control ideas is the chemical process area. Chemical plants often contain several hundred controllers in one production unit. The preferred control algorithm is the single-loop proportional-integral-derivative controller. Recently, more advanced algorithms such as delay compensators, state estimators, noninteracting multivariable controllers have begun to spread in the chemical industry. Many commercial chemical process control manufacturers now offer self-tuning and adaptive controllers.

- Hot strip mills in the steel industry were one of the earliest successes of computer control. High product volume coupled with the requirements of high and uniform product quality were among the factors that led to computer automation as early as 1961. Since then, computer control systems for hot strip mills have advanced to a mature engineering product featuring multilevel, multivariable adaptive control. Precision achieved by these systems made possible the rolling of high strength steel suitable for the harsh environment of the Alaska Pipeline. The widespread use of this computer control technology is exemplified by the fact that General Electric alone has supplied well over 50 such computer automation projects worldwide.

Control systems are also increasingly present in many consumer products and affect the lifestyle of society. For example:

- The automotive field is on the verge of becoming a big user of modern control systems. A few years ago, the antilock brake system based on feedback control principles became a success story in some car designs. Now it is about to become a standard feature of many models. The next few years will witness a widespread introduction of control microprocessors into passenger cars. As a result, new cars will have many attractive features due to control systems. These features will include: integrated engine and transmission control, automatic suspension control that will improve both ride and handling, traction control that will combine power-train controls and antilock braking, and a variable-assist steering system that will give a firm, secure feel at high speeds but will make steering easy when parking.

- Commercial airliners are equipped with many control systems, including digital autopilots designed by methods based on linear state feedback theory.

- Disk drives in computers, videocassette machines, sewing machines, and electronic typewriters are all equipped with servomechanisms which have microprocessor chips performing the control functions.

- A new design of artificial hearts includes a microcomputer-based control system in which the control philosophy consists of P-wave synchronization and stabilization of trial pressures by means of a self-tuning controller.

- Climate control in large modern buildings is maintained by central computerized systems with many sensors and actuators.

On knowledge transfer

In control theory, as in other sciences, the transfer of knowledge from theory to applications occurs by various, often convoluted, and unanticipated paths. Research on fundamental theoretical problems often proceeds on a different time scale than research on applications.

Moreover, the most striking applications of a theory are often not the ones that motivated it. The connection between a theoretical result and an important application is often made by someone other than the inventor of the theory, and frequently only after a period of several years.

Sometimes the transfer of knowledge between theory and applications is facilitated by experts working in close communication, allowing theoretical issues and practical considerations to influence each other in an interactive mode. More often, however, a slower, "diffusive" mechanism is responsible.

For example, an established investigator develops a theory and teaches his findings at his university. He supervises several graduate students who write theses on topics related to the investigator's research. These former students go on to other organizations (academic and industrial) where they apply the new knowledge. This mode of knowledge transfer is a gradual process, involving an evolution of ideas and the sociology of the field. Thus the application of new mathematical concepts in control theory is generally not immediate: it is necessarily not only to test the new concepts in practice, but also to achieve a critical mass of experts who believe in the new concepts.

Status of the profession

Scientists who work in control theory can be found in various departments at universities, in industry, and in some specialized institutes. Those with highly theoretical or mathematical interests are usually employed by mathematical science departments and to a lesser extent by electrical, aerospace, and mechanical engineering departments.

There are several professional societies with interest in control. The Society for Industrial and Applied Mathematics (SIAM) has a Special Interest Group in control theory, and publishes one of the main scientific journals in this area, the *SIAM Journal on Control and Optimization*. This journal is regarded by many as a leading journal in the mathematics of control theory.

The Institute of Electrical and Electronics Engineers (IEEE) has the largest number of members working in control and systems. They are grouped in the Control Systems Society of IEEE. The membership of that society is about 10,000, including theoretical scientists, computer scientists, and engineers. IEEE publishes the journal *IEEE Transactions on Automatic Control*, which has a theoretical flavor.

Recently, Springer International has launched a new journal, *Mathematics of Control, Signals, and Systems*, which aims at publishing mathematically sophisticated papers in control and signal processing. Since it spans a broad range of topics, this journal is likely to become an important forum for new mathematical ideas in control.

Several organizations cooperate in the annual Conference on Decision and Control, which attracts about 600 or more participants. Many sessions at that conference are devoted to mathematical aspects of control. In addition, many SIAM and American Mathematical Society (AMS) conferences have topics and sessions on the mathematics of control.

In addition to the United States and Canada, mathematical control theory has been well represented in European countries. European contributions are impressive, both in numbers and quality; the strength of the European research in control has grown in the last decade. The largest western European institute with a focus in control is the National Research Institute in Computer Science and Automation (INRIA) in France, which does research in computer science, control, and in applied mathematics and computation. INRIA has about 800 employees, including a very active group of young mathematicians and computer scientists. It has provided an excellent example of the use of mathematics in advanced industrial applications. In Italy, there is an active engineering control community, and Italian mathematicians have provided many important ideas in mathematical aspects of control theory. Great Britain and Poland have substantial research efforts in both mathematical and system engineering aspects of control, with a number of important contributions on record in areas such as multivariable, nonlinear, stochastic, optimal control, infinite-dimensional systems, and hierarchical systems. In the Netherlands, systems and control theory has become one of the recognized areas of mathematics. There is a vigorous research effort in this area, a graduate program on the national level, and control courses are often part of the undergraduate curricula. Swedish researchers have taken the lead in the use of self-tuning regulators and adaptive control methods in industrial process control. In West Germany, in addition to a solid base in industrial control there is a recognized feeling that it is essential to enhance research efforts in mathematical control theory.

In the USSR major control institutes have existed for a long time, and control theory, systems, and automation have long been recognized as areas of priority in research. The status of Soviet science in this area has been surveyed in the report, "Soviet Applied Mathematics Research: Mathematical Theory of Systems, Control, and Statistical Signal Processing," published by Science Applications, Inc. in

1984. According to that report "the quality of mathematical research in the Soviet Union in the area included in this report is very high, with some of the best Soviet mathematicians deeply involved. In a number of specific areas, the Soviet work is assessed to be more advanced than that in the United States."

Japanese work in this field has been accelerating recently and exhibits good interactions between mathematics and engineering. Several universities offer professorships in "mathematical engineering," including control theory. The Japanese have made interesting advances in robust control, in discrete-event systems, and in the design of flexible manufacturing systems. In fact, computer software for automated factory design, written in the C language, was developed and offered commercially by a Japanese company.

There is often a great deal of complementary research being done in various countries; therefore, international meetings and joint research projects may be effective in accelerating progress in this field. The congress of IFAC (International Federation of Automatic Control) serves as a very useful forum for exchange of ideas.

Educational aspects and training of new PhD's

In the sixties, control theory was practiced and taught predominantly in electrical engineering departments. One benefit was the high level of mathematical sophistication of the students traditionally attracted to the electrical engineering profession. The students' training was influenced by applications arising from industrial contacts. There was also a significant involvement of aerospace, mechanical, and chemical engineering departments in the training process. Since the late sixties and seventies, control theory has become more widely recognized as part of mathematics, and more new control theory PhD's are receiving mathematical degrees. Today, mathematical research in control theory can be relatively abstract, so much so that the connection with the original motivating problem is sometimes lost. Nonetheless, increased mathematical rigor has helped to attract gifted minds to the field, has given control theory more powerful mathematical tools which have made its results more widely applicable, and has enhanced its standing among other mathematical disciplines.

Today, the diversity of mathematical techniques employed in control theory has implications for the training of new scientists. It is increasingly difficult to do innovative research in control by using only one mathematical approach. Instead, it is becoming necessary for new PhD's to be aware of many complementary mathematical techniques, and also of research in other areas such as nonlinear dynamical systems, computational mathematics, and computer science. Such diverse training requirements mean that few schools are equipped to provide the necessary knowledge.

While exact statistics on the number of mathematicians that are being trained in this field in the U.S. are not available, the comments heard through the Panel indicated that the numbers are far too low. Though the problem is not limited to this particular area of study, the additional requirements described above make the situation particularly acute.

Ideally, training of young control scientists should occur in an environment where there are interactions between mathematics and engineering. This depends on a critical mass of faculty in both mathematical science and engineering departments, and an institutional atmosphere which rewards such interdisciplinary cooperation. In some instances, existing departmental barriers inhibit this process.

A survey of existing departments and schools in the U.S. done through the Panel discussion showed that mathematical scientists working in control tend to be scattered in various universities without a major concentration. There are only a few places in the U.S. where a candidate for a PhD can learn a variety of (mathematical) techniques of control theory, and where there is an ongoing collaboration between mathematicians and control engineers. In some other countries, notably the USSR and France, there exist centers providing such opportunities. Strengthening of the U.S. role in this field will require enhancing the existing effort through the creation of interdisciplinary centers with a critical mass of researchers and educators.

CHAPTER 3. RESEARCH NEEDS AND
OPPORTUNITIES

Control theory is now entering an exciting stage in its development. Advances in computer and instrumentation technology are creating opportunities for new applications of the existing theory. At the same time, the field faces unprecedented challenges on two fronts. First, scientific and technological progress is demanding innovative uses of control theory in many new applications, for which the established methods are insufficient. Second, important fundamental problems within the field remain unsolved and new ideas are needed to make further advances.

In examining these issues, the Panel identified a number of important application areas, or "Research Needs," to which mathematical and computational research in control theory can make significant contributions. After reviewing the present status of basic research in various areas of control theory, the Panel members wrote the vignettes which appear in Chapter 4. The Panel then discussed current trends within the field, and these are discussed in the section "Research Opportunities."

Research needs in modern science and technology

- Large space structures.

These include a new generation of spacecraft with very large flexible components such as solar collectors, dish antennas, radar arrays, truss structures, space telescopes, and space stations. In general, these structures are characterized by weak damping, and interconnection of rigid and flexible parts. The tasks of controlling the rotation, pointing with high accuracy, and stabilizing the vibrations in the absence of damping pose difficult control problems, where theoretical and computational advances are needed. Current challenges include the following problems: (i) Structures will frequently change configuration, for example, by a deployment of a magnetometer boom and solar panel, by shuttle docking and take off, etc. Therefore, an on-board system identification for each new configuration is an important requirement. (ii) Control laws for flexible bodies combined with rigid body attachments need to be developed. (iii) Robust control schemes for distributed parameter systems are needed to compensate for unmodeled dynamics and uncertain parameters.

- Robotics.

The utility of robotics depends in large part on the efficiency and accuracy of computer algorithms controlling the robots. The cost of computations required in the kinematic and dynamic calculations is high and limits the speed and versatility of robotic manipulation. At present, only simple robotic tasks can be automatically controlled in real-time. The design of more complicated robots will require an improved understanding of the dynamics and control of nonlinear systems with many degrees of freedom. Fundamental advances in the area of robustness of nonlinear control are needed to achieve stability of robotic functions in the presence of disturbances (e.g., vertical stability of a walking robot in the presence of wind gusts). Also, computer vision and the linkage of visual sensing to the control of robot motion need development. Finally, a difficult challenge will be the cooperative control of multiple arms. The questions of motion planning in the common space, jamming avoidance, force control on holding a common object, and robustness are rich areas to be explored.

- Power Systems and Computer Networks.

The control of electrical power generating and distribution systems required decisions at a number of different locations. The geographically distributed controllers must work with detailed local information but limited sharing of knowledge about the system as a whole. The deregulation of the system operation in the U.S. has increased the interdependency of various parts of the system. The new operating modes involve more dynamic inputs to the system and cause it to work closer to the limits of capacity. This has created a need for new research on control strategies for large interconnected systems. Similar issues arise in computer networks and complex air traffic control systems. These applications demand new theories of distributed (or decentralized) information processing and decision making.

● Combustion Control.

This area is technologically important as it relates to the design
of new engines for aviation and space industries, and to the control
of other combustion processes. One of the significant problems here
is the control of combustion instability, such as that encountered in
liquid propellant rocket engines. The unstable combustion is generally accompanied by appreciable acoustic disturbances. Past efforts
to suppress this instability were directed at geometrical changes in
the system so as to interfere with the acoustic-combustion interaction
responsible for the instability, or at the design of damping and dissi-
pating devices. The active control of combustion instability by heat
addition or subtraction, or by acoustic control, may open new possibilities, posing at the same time new theoretical and implementation
problems. While the modeling of combustion by analytical and computational means is a current research topic in applied mathematics,
there is relatively little control theoretic knowledge on how to control combustion and reaction-diffusion phenomena. A major application in this area will be active combustion control in the National
Aerospace Plane, where unprecedented difficulties will arise because
of great variability of flight conditions.

● Fluid Flow Control.

The interaction of control and fluid dynamics is an area that
awaits mathematical and large-scale computational development. For
example, in some aeroelastic control problems such as airflow over
an aircraft wing, the flap movement caused by control changes the
dynamics of the flow and deforms the wing. The structural and
fluid dynamics are coupled together and they are coupled with the
dynamics of the control system. At present there is no model that
takes into account all these factors. While for conventional aircraft
the dynamic interactions described above can in fact be considered
as practically decoupled, there are aircraft where such effects cannot
be ignored. The design of advanced aircraft in the future may require
that active fluid flow control be considered, including options such
as controlled heating filaments on wings to prevent turbulence. Very
little is known about modelling fluid flow for the purpose of control,
or about the control paradigms that may arise in such contexts.

● Control of plasma.

The achievement of a controlled fusion reaction would contribute to a solution of the world's energy problems. Large efforts are devoted to research on fusion in the U.S., Europe, Japan, and the USSR. The most promising approach is to confine an ionized gas (plasma) with huge electromagnets in machines called tokomaks. The fundamental problem is to hold a very high density plasma at a high temperature in a desired configuration for long periods of time in spite of plasma instabilities. Information from sensors is used to effect rapid and precise changes in the strength of the coil currents to compensate for disturbances which disrupt the plasma. The main difficulty lies not with the hardware, since it is already in place on functioning tokomaks, but with algorithms for using sensor information to control coil currents. The mathematical models of the plasma instabilities and the mathematics of control for free boundary problems are not yet sufficiently understood. Some effort has been devoted to the control of plasma shape in France and Japan, but major challenges remain. Identification problems are also important in tokomaks, because measurements are difficult to make, and because knowledge of transport coefficients is required to calculate a correct energy balance. Significant improvement in the control and identification of plasma could cut the cost of future reactors dramatically and possibly make the difference between success and failure of this approach to energy generation.

- Solidification processes.

Explosive growth in materials science led recently to extensive studies of the process of alloy solidification. Understanding and subsequently controlling such processes is of fundamental importance for the quality of new materials. The critical issues in the process of solidification are the shape and stability of the solid-liquid interface. A non-planar interface may cause nonuniform density of the solute, leading to a nonuniform, substandard product. There are several sources of instabilities, such as convection, nonuniform concentration gradients, surface tensions, and constitutional supercooling. Recently, sophisticated mathematical methods have begun to play a role in the study of these instabilities. Mathematical models include a coupled system of nonlinear partial differential equations for heat and mass transport, the Navier-Stokes equations for the liquid phase, and a free boundary problem to describe the behavior of the interface. There are two control issues in this context: the problem of reconstructing the interface from indirect measurements, and the problem of controlling the interface by controlling heating, the magnetic field, the electric field, and rotation of the alloy in the furnace. Computational modeling of such processes involves supercomputers and may evolve into a "numerical furnace." This opens exciting possibilities for studies of control problems.

● Steel Industry.

The American Institute of Steel Engineering has formulated a challenge in the area of dynamic control of hot strip mills. In order to obtain high grade steel that meets present competitive international standards, one needs to control precisely the temperature profile in the hot strip of steel during its cooling phase. The hot strip, typically 3mm thick, exits the finishing mill at a speed of 1000 ft/min. It is conveyed over a 400 ft long runout table where it is flooded top and bottom with jets of water. When the strip's front end enters the coiler, the strip and the machinery (the finishing mill, the runout table, and the coiler) is jointly accelerated to a speed of 4000 ft/min. The challenge lies in the conceptual design of a control strategy for the strip speed and cooling jet flow rates. The control must dynamically maintain the optimal temperature profile along the strip on the runout table, both in the constant speed phase and in the acceleration phase. Precision of the control system is directly related to the product quality, and thus to the competitive position of steel manufacturers.

● Biomedical Research.

The use of system theoretic concepts in medicine has a substantial potential, but the progress in this area is slow due to communication barriers between fields. In general, regulation of physiological variables is governed by the same feedback principles as in man-made systems, but the lack of precise models and great variability of data from one organism to another make the application of quantitative methods very difficult. However, the understanding of physiological dynamics and internal nonlinear interactions may lead to better design of therapies such as hormonal, drug, and radiation therapies. Design of portable insulin pumps equipped with control chips is an example. Design of prosthetic devices such as artificial limbs, equipped with microelectronic controllers is another area where the input from control theory is desirable.

● Optimal Design of Structures and Materials.

Difficult questions arise in the design of large structures. For example, how should a small amount of viscoelastic material be placed so as to achieve maximal passive damping? How to design a shape of a thermal diffuser in a telecommunications satellite so as to minimize the weight for given specification of temperature distribution?

In composite materials, how to design a microgeometry of fiber reinforcements so as to optimize average mechanical parameters of a beam or a plate? These questions lead to new variational methods that are closely related to those arising in optimal control theory.

- Hydrology.

This science deals with problems governing water supply for domestic use, agriculture, industry, and natural resource maintenance. Water management efforts include the control of aquifer quantity and quality. Large-scale mathematical models have been developed to monitor drainage areas and surface water supply. Finite difference simulators and models based on partial differential equations have been proposed. In either case, parameters such as porosity and permeability may exhibit variability over a large spatial domain. This makes the modeling alone computationally difficult. Control aspects arise in two ways: in the parameter identification problem, and in the design of management strategies. Major unsolved problems are: choice of models that minimize the effects of ill-conditioning in the parameter identification, methods to determine the best sensing locations and placement of wells for both injection and recovery, and methods to design feedback control strategies that take into account the scale and nonlinearities of the model.

- Oil Recovery.

As in hydrology, there are substantial modeling efforts underway in the area of underground reservoir simulation. The purpose of modeling in petroleum applications is to optimize the recovery of minerals and hydrocarbon from underground permeable reservoirs. Predicting the performance of the reservoir under various exploitation or production schemes is an important part of that process. This requires accurate modeling which in turn requires having effective and robust methods for solving inverse problems, including parameter estimation. Moreover, in enhanced oil recovery processes, the control of the movement of the interface between the injected and resident fluids is critical in optimizing the total yield.

- Economics.

Computerized economic models are increasingly being used to

guide economic decision making. Many models exist or are being developed by large private companies, government agencies, and international organizations. In the U.S., the Congressional Budget Office and Federal Reserve Board maintain several models to make projections and assist in policy formation. Certain national banks use dynamic models to track currency fluctuations. Economic models have a different character from most of those used in other sciences, because in economics there are no theories capable of predicting events with high accuracy, and experiments cannot be made to verify theory. However, certain economic models have much in common with stochastic control models. Much of the economic theory consists of predicting implications for the economy as a whole of individual consumption and investment policies. Equilibrium analysis is of major importance. These models, combined with large-scale computational implementation, may play an increasing role in understanding economic phenomena. Methods of stochastic control and dynamic stochastic optimization are likely to play an increasing role in these models.

- Manufacturing Systems.

Contemporary highly automated manufacturing systems are often designed as flexible systems, to allow for changing demands and to adapt to changes in production planning, changes in supplies, and failures of machines. The increased flexibility and efficiency is achieved at the price of increased complexity of the system. Computer-controlled workstations can be rapidly switched from one task to another, and the routings of parts between the stations can be altered. The system is controlled by a central computer or by a network of local computers. Although several such systems are operating in industry, the design, scheduling and control issues are not completely understood. Existing analytical models are often too simple to handle the complexity involved while ad hoc designs based on simulations of realistic models do not add up to a systematic design methodology. The need for such a methodology exists, and there have been various attempts to address it by using approaches such as queuing network models, decomposition methods, and hierarchical control structures. Expert systems tools have also been proposed. Conceptual innovations in this area may have substantial impact on engineering design methods.

- Performance Evaluation of Computer Systems.

While the development of hardware for multiprocessing is con-

tinuing at a rapid pace, methods for evaluating the performance of
various new computing systems are not well understood. Available
performance evaluation tools (software packages) are based on the
representation of computer systems in terms of queuing network theory. Three different types of techniques are provided: analytical solutions based on product form queuing network theory, numerical solutions based on Markov process formulation, and simulations based
on a discrete-event approach. The basic primitives of parallel algorithms and distributed applications are not incorporated in the tools
presently available. A new set of models is needed. Also, methods
based on simulation or Markovian solution fail on parallel systems
due to combinatorial explosion problems. It is thus important that
new methods be developed to cope with the large dimensionality
of parallel systems and their synchronization constraints. Elements
of multiserver queuing theory and stochastic comparison techniques
have been suggested as possibilities for the analysis of processor networks of large dimension. These techniques have much in common
with methods of discrete-event stochastic control.

- Computer-Aided Design of Control Systems.

Many industrial and space applications are generating control
system performance requirements of unprecedented complexity and
stringency. Some of these requirements can only be met by integrated design techniques which treat the plant and its control system as a single unit. As a result, the importance of computer-aided
design techniques and interactive computer-aided design systems is
growing at a very fast pace. Computer-aided control-system design
research is a highly interdisciplinary activity which involves control
theory, computer science, numerical analysis, and optimization. Current research needs include the newly emerging computation-oriented
control theory, computer graphics for the display of abstract multidimensional information, efficient iterative simulation of dynamical
systems of large complexity, optimization algorithms for design, and
software integration.

Research opportunities

Future directions: a general view

The research needs presented in the previous section exhibit an
overwhelming diversity. While each new application raises its own
unique set of questions, the ensemble of these applications has several
common themes that indicate new, or known but unsolved problems
of control theory. We discuss these themes briefly in very general

terms.

A common theme for most advanced applications is the *complexity* of systems to be controlled. The complexity reveals itself at many levels, for instance in the overall system structure, in the variety of kinds of information to be processed (deterministic and stochastic signals, images, and symbolic information), and in the complexity of physical phenomena to be controlled, such as combustion or fluid flow. There is no general theory of complex systems and it is unlikely that there will be one in the foreseeable future. However, complexity will continue to provide intellectual stimulation and challenge for research. The coming years will witness a great deal of effort devoted to development of new approaches to handle complexity in control problems. Some of these efforts might rely on the concepts of computer science: data structures and algorithms, computational complexity, and distributed and parallel computation. Other efforts may turn to new tools such as neural networks, whose potential in control problems remains to be discovered. Most likely, however, there will be a greatly increased emphasis on approaches that represent a blend of theoretical, experimental, and computational work, in which the availability of new computing technologies will play an increasing role.

Large-scale computation, which is a common tool in fluid dynamics and other fields of science, has only recently begun to make its presence visible in control theory research. Used as a tool to replace costly and risky on-line experiments, large-scale computational simulation of complex real processes is likely to open new ways of exploring new control paradigms. So far, supercomputers have been used in control and identification problems arising in large space structures, but many other control problems described in previous sections lend themselves to large-scale computational analysis. This approach will require the use of advanced mathematical modeling techniques, which include asymptotics, numerical analysis, and computation. In some cases, models of important processes will have to be validated through control-oriented laboratory experiments. This approach, a *control-oriented large-scale computation*, is thus another common theme for many new control problems.

More on the theoretical side, the examples described in the preceding section show that one of the great challenges of control theory is *control of nonlinear systems with many degrees of freedom*. Such systems arise, for instance, in robotics, where systems may have a large but finite number of degrees of freedom, and in large space structures, combustion control, and fluid flow control, where the number of degrees of freedom is infinite. The challenge is not only in the conceptual development of control laws for nonlinear systems, but also in making the control computable and robust with respect to model uncertainties and changes. Although recent developments in the area of control of finite- dimensional nonlinear systems have been quite intense, there is still a need for a better understanding of the fundamental dynamics of nonlinear control. Presently, this understanding is limited to low-dimensional systems. Current developments in nonlinear dynamical systems without control show that even quite simple systems may have very complex behavior caused by nonlinear phenomena. Nonlinear systems with many degrees of freedom thus represent a vast area with an abundance of difficult control problems. Exploring potential connections between control theory and theory of nonlinear dynamical systems (including nonlinear partial differential equations) is likely to lead to significant advances in both fields. This is likely to be a prominent theme of control research in the next decade.

The themes of *adaptive, self-organizing* and *intelligent control* will likely increase in importance as the tools to implement these concepts become more widely available. Our present understanding of the fundamental laws of automatic adaptation is very limited. Several technological developments, for example the National Aerospace Plane, will require development of new control principles with strong adaptive features. The theory of adaptive control is likely to interact strongly with the theory of nonlinear dynamical systems. Closer to engineering aspects of control, the integration of numeric, symbolic, and optical information in a dynamic feedback loop is a barrier to overcome in the development of advanced robotic systems and intelligent control systems. Advances in theory and computation are likely to contribute to substantial payoffs in this area.

The theme of *stochastic control* will increasingly be present in many applications, such as economics, power systems, and manufacturing. New theoretical and computational approaches related to stochastic control and to new developments in random processes are likely to have substantial impact on techniques of signal and image processing. This will affect indirectly a broad range of applications. Estimation, identification, and stochastic adaptive systems will likely continue to be very active areas of research. Those areas are likely to benefit greatly from the availability of massive parallel computing, where each processor may be programmed to compute a different realization of a stochastic process.

The description of these themes is not intended to be complete, nor is there any attempt to forecast which areas of research will produce discoveries of major importance. As is true in any area of science, new discoveries and their impact cannot be predicted. One can forecast, however, that continued progress will depend critically on maintaining strong ties between the mathematical and engineering aspects of control science. Lacking such ties, opportunities will be missed to discover novel approaches to control problems from modern science and technology, and to bring to bear appropriate mathematical tools. When the engineering interface is weak, mathematical research in control may focus on producing more refined versions of existing theory. These considerations imply, in particular, that a healthy inderdisciplinary environment is essential for training the next generation of control theorists.

Specific research opportunities

Some of the more immediate research directions and opportunities can be identified by extrapolating current trends. This section contains descriptions of such research opportunities in various areas corresponding approximately to the areas defined by the vignettes contained in the next chapter. The descriptions of opportunities in various areas is not of uniform length. This is largely a function of the written material provided by Panel members and submitted to the Panel by external respondents. It is not intended to reflect perceived relative importance of various opportunities. The present status of various research areas, and specific research opportunities, are described in greater detail in Chapter 4.

- Robust and Adaptive Control.

Although the development of better mathematical models for applications is, and should continue to be, a major goal of control scientists, it is essential to remember that is impossible to describe the dynamics of most real systems by exact mathematical models. In the presence of such modeling uncertainties and unmeasurable disturbances, feedback control is an extremely effective approach to control design. In fact, it is fair to say that a fundamental reason for using feedback is to accomplish performance objectives in the presence of uncertainty. The use of feedback to stabilize unstable (open-loop) systems has been applied recently to statically unstable aircraft (F-16,X-29) and will play a major role in future designs. Feedback control in the face of uncertainty will remain an important area of control research. It is also one of the most active and promising areas today.

In this area, there are two research directions that are both practically important and mathematically interesting. One of them is the theory of robust control. Recent progress in that area involving operator theory and H^∞- approach reveal the power and depth of new methods. Continuation of this direction is likely to produce new results, particularly in the area of multivariable systems and systems with delays. The development of robust control theory for nonlinear dynamical systems and for the boundary control of partial differential equations remains a major challenge of substantial importance.

The second direction is that of adaptive control. While important new results have been obtained in the last several years, there are some major unresolved issues that will provide interesting opportunities for both theoretical and applied research. Adaptive control is a necessity in systems that exhibit great variability of parameters over the range of working conditions. The newest example of such a system is the flight control system for the National Aerospace Plane, which will fly at altitudes ranging from 0 to 150,000 feet. Conceptual advances and new computer capabilities may make adaptive control a powerful tool of tomorrow's technology.

- Control of Distributed Parameter Systems.

It is expected that the emphasis in this area will gradually shift from linear models to more complicated nonlinear systems such as those important in nonlinear elasticity and fluid dynamics. However, there are still many problems in the control of linear distributed parameter systems that need to be addressed.

For example, a theory of robust control for linear infinite-dimensional systems needs to be developed. The recent developments in H^∞ control for robust stability of finite-dimensional systems could lead to very useful and practical tools if these ideas can be extended to distributed parameter systems. In fact, all of the fundamental questions in finite-dimensional control theory (robustness, adaptive control, stochastic control, nonlinearity, etc.) remain important in distributed parameter control and new mathematical questions appear because of the infinite-dimensional nature of the system.

The control of distributed parameter systems has the potential to give impetus, not only to the applications, but also to other areas of mathematics, mechanics, and fluid dynamics. For example, research in the control of lightly damped structures has already raised many fundamental questions about the nature of "material damping," a topic in continuum mechanics. Recent advances in the theory of nonlinear partial differential equations, Hamiltonian systems, computational algorithms, computer power, and modeling make distributed parameter control an area ripe with possibilities for important breakthroughs.

- Nonlinear Systems.

The control of nonlinear dynamical systems governed by ordinary differential equations, with several control and output variables, is and will continue to be an important topic. Robotics and helicopter autopilots are typically quoted as applications, but nonlinear dynamical systems are so pervasive that the importance of this area is easily taken for granted. Nonlinear control systems will in general also include infinite-dimensional systems governed by nonlinear partial differential equations, etc., if the inputs and outputs are finite-dimensional. The last topic area is not yet very well developed. One of the main challenges in these areas is the understanding of dynamics and feedback in systems with many degrees of freedom.

In the immediate future, there are at least three important mathematical trends that are likely to furnish new ideas:

First, the control of smooth nonlinear dynamical systems based on differential geometry methods presents several problems: 1. Approximations of nonlinear systems. The approximation of the input-output map defined by a system initialized at given point on a differentiable manifold is an unsolved problem. Recent work on hypoellipticity of differential operators and local controllability indicates that there is some promise in the approximations of a Lie algebra of vector fields on the manifold M, but more research needs to be done. 2. Local controllability. Recent sufficient conditions have relied on some approximation techniques for Lie algebras to reduce the problem to one which is almost entirely algebraic and yet is still unsolved. 3. Stabilization of nonlinear systems. Traditional techniques, including Lyapunov methods, are of limited power, but center manifold techniques are also currently achieving success. The nontrivial cases correspond to situations in which system linearization around the initial state is not stabilizable. A method to calculate stabilizing feedbacks would be of major importance. New methods drawn from differential geometry, foliations, and nonlinear dynamics are currently offering significant contributions.

The second trend is based on ideas of nonsmooth analysis and set-valued differential inclusions. The recently developed differential calculus of set-valued maps and advances in differential inclusions have opened the way to analyze control of nonlinear systems in which the nonlinear functions are not differentiable. "Conical derivatives" of set-valued maps may be the right tools for analysis of controllability and optimality. Recently proved inverse function theorems for set-valued maps have led to new results on local controllability and maximum principles for nonsmooth dynamical systems. Relations with the Lie-algebraic approach have been discovered. Problems with state constraints, historically considered to be hard, can be analyzed by this approach. Research in this area is likely to have an impact on problems involving nonlinear infinite-dimensional systems. Numerical methods for this approach are an open area of study; ideas from nondifferentiable optimization, such as epiconvergence, may be useful.

The third set of ideas is related to the solvability of the Hamilton-Jacobi-Bellman equation which arises via the dynamic programming method for optimal control. Recent progress on viscosity solutions holds some promise here. The viscosity solutions method has streamlined today's thinking about the H-J-B equation, and provides powerful ways of proving uniqueness of solutions which may be nonsmooth or even discontinuous, as well as continuous dependence of viscosity solutions on the problem model. The translation of results about viscosity solutions into constructive results applicable to the feedback synthesis problem would be of substantial utility to control science. In addition, viscosity solution methods play an increasing role in asymptotic problems for nonlinear partial differential equations, such as reaction-diffusion equations and the equations of stochastic control and large deviation theory.

- Stochastic Control.

The areas of stochastic control and recursive nonlinear estimation are motivated by applications in such diverse areas as aerospace guidance and control, signal processing and communications, manufacturing processes, and financial economics. There are well developed mathematical theories of optimal stochastic control and nonlinear filtering, especially for models, based on stochastic differential equations and Markov diffusion processes. These theoretical developments in turn gave impetus to research in probability theory and partial differential equations.

A long-standing problem has been to find practically implementable algorithms for stochastic control and nonlinear estimation. One need is for further research on techniques for numerical solution of the dynamic programming equations for large Markov chains and the Hamilton-Jacobi-Bellman partial differential equation for controlled diffusions. Other approaches include asymptotic analyses for problems with incomplete or partial observations, and expert system methods. Research which exploits special model structures and alternative computational approaches to the usual dynamic programming is needed. Another need is for decentralized stochastic control and information processing algorithms, since in many practical systems decisions are taken and computations performed by processors located at physically distinct sites.

Naive use of Markov diffusion processes can lead to erroneous results. This happened, for example, in analyses of the large-time behavior of phase-locked loops in communication theory. What is needed are careful analyses of the correct Markov diffusion limits from more realistic models arising, for example, in communication systems with correlated noise, or in queuing systems.

There is a need to develop methods appropriate for the control of discrete-event dynamical systems, such as those arising in computer/communication networks and production or assembly lines. Typical kinds of control actions involve scheduling of tasks, routing of messages and dynamic resource allocation. Queuing and multiarm bandit models have provided interesting results in some cases, using such techniques as perturbation analyses, Gittens index theory, and heavy traffic diffusion approximations. This area is likely to provide many challenging problems for stochastic control in the future. In particular, it is currently stimulating interesting research in singular stochastic control theory.

Problems of dynamic decision-making under uncertainty in management science and economics continue to provide interesting research topics in stochastic control. The popularity of the Black-Scholes model for pricing of stock options has led to much interest in stochastic control and optimal stopping models in financial economics. Other areas of application include hydrology and fishery management.

Many of the signal processing problems of greatest current and future technological interest involve processing of spatially distributed data (estimation for random fields.) One area is computational vision, which has important applications including robotics and visual inspection systems. Another area involves so-called inverse problems, including those of nondestructive testing and medical imaging. The control community has an opportunity to contribute in these areas.

• Optimal Design of Distributed Parameter Systems.

Many areas of modern technology lead to problems involving the optimization of shape or material composition. In the aerospace and automotive industries a frequent goal is to minimize weight by making efficient use of the available materials. In biomedical inverse problems and nondestructive testing the goal is typically to infer the interior composition of a body by means of acoustic, electrical, or other measurements at the boundary. A third area of application is the modeling of plasmas and fluids, where the location of an unknown free boundary can often be determined by solving an appropriate shape optimization problem. These can all be viewed as examples of optimal controls, in which the state is governed by a partial differential equation of mathematical physics such as Maxwell's equations or linear elasticity. Being controlled is the shape of the domain on which the PDE is to be solved, or else the coefficients of the equation, representing the material composition of the structure.

A current successful application has been to the shape optimization of automotive parts. Since large stresses generally lead to crack growth and failure, it is typical to constrain the pointwise maximum of the linearly elastic stress. Codes have been developed at General Motors, Renault, and elsewhere for decreasing the weight of a structure subject to constraints on its displacement, compliance, or maximum stress under specified loads. With the current generation of supercomputers it is possible to solve even three-dimensional problems, using a finite element approximation for the elasticity system and a special-purpose algorithm for the associated finite-dimensional nonlinear optimization.

Mathematical scientists have much to offer to such efforts, especially with regard to the appropriateness of the model and the accuracy of the computation. For example, when can one trust the value of the maximum stress obtained using a finite element code? Special attention is due when using a description that is only asymptotically valid, such as a plate or shell theory: in such cases an attempt at optimization may in fact merely take advantage of the errors in the model.

A promising new idea is concerned with the optimal design of composite materials, obtained for example by perforation or fiber reinforcement. Here the goal is to choose a microgeometry which extremizes some feature of the composite's macroscopic or average properties. There is a direct link to large-scale problems of optimal design, by considering structures that are composed of optimally chosen composite materials, varying from point to point as required by the loads. The analysis and optimization of composites is a relatively new topic, and its mathematical development, based on the theory of homogenization, has barely begun. Nevertheless it is expected to have significant impact on certain classes of design problems in the near future.

Looking ahead, we envision an almost unending variety of applications, each presenting its own mathematical challenge. In the design of a large space structure, how should a small amount of viscoelastic material be placed so as to achieve maximal passive damping? Can one adjust the shape of an airplane, or coat it with an appropriately chosen material, to reduce its visibility to radar? Can one determine the interior composition of a three-dimensional body by means of voltage and current measurements on the boundary (a technique called electric current computed tomography)?

It should be noted that all of our examples have been static: computational limitations make it difficult, even with today's supercomputers, to solve dynamic control problems involving partial differential equations in two or more space dimensions. This, however, can be expected to change. For example, airplane wing profiles are already being designed by an optimization procedure based on the equations of transonic flow. Perhaps the wing of the future will be deformable, and that optimization will be done not on the ground but continuously in time.

- Computational Methods For Control.

The study of computational methods for control offers many unique mathematical challenges. The key point to keep always in mind is that in addition to "traditional" numerical analytic problems, there are other constraints that must be addressed when investigating computational methods for control (e.g., real-time, minimal storage, on-line, and fault tolerant computing). The elementary idea of conditioning, although well-studied and analyzed for a wide variety of numerical problems, is not well understood for many of the most basic control problems. For example, while there exist effective numerical algorithms for the solution of matrix Riccati equations, an understanding of the condition of these problems is still lacking. There are many open questions on convergence and stability of algorithms in control and substantial research will be required to remedy this situation.

Other issues that need to be addressed are the effects of finite precision, finite range arithmetic on the software (and hardware) implementation of control algorithms. The development of computational algorithms for large sparse systems remains an important research topic. In general, the requirements that control algorithms be implemented in real-time and on-line present several numerical problems that are unique to control and which call for considerable research in fast and reliable algorithms.

- Computational Challenges to Control of Partial Differential Equations.

A major challenge is the reduction of an infinite-dimensional problem governed by partial differential equations (or inequalities) to a finite- dimensional one. For the most complicated problems (such as combustion and/or turbulence phenomena) even the numerical simulation methods (i.e., the methods solving the state equations) are far from satisfactory. Moreover, even for linear problems, it may occur that the best simulation methods are not always well suited for being integrated in a control loop: often, very accurate methods involve automatic mesh refinement, tuning of parameters, etc., which make these methods not very robust.

Another challenge is dimensionality, particularly for three dimensional problems and coupled systems of nonlinear equations modeling stiff phenomena (combustion, semi-conductors). In some cases the time and space discretization steps can be very small, leading to enormous finite-dimensional systems. In this direction the use of domain decomposition techniques, implicit-explicit time integration methods, multi-level methods, and vector and parallel computing are relevant to solve the state equations; however, the integration of these methods in a control loop leads to nontrivial theoretical and practical problems.

Yet another challenge is related to the geometry of the spatial domain, which may be moving in time, or may be an unknown, as in the shape optimization problem. This leads to significant representation problems to be combined with the difficulties already mentioned above.

- Optimal Control and Design Algorithm.

In the area of optimal control and design, there exist numerous opportunities for research on efficient, computer-implementable algorithms. Control, shape, state-space, and frequency constraints tend to lead to optimal control problems of enormous computational complexity. The resolution of this difficulty will very likely take advantage of the fact that the iterations of an optimal control algorithm generate large numbers of neighboring trajectories.

In many instances the cost function is not differentiable with respect to the control variables; these are clearly situations for which nonsmooth optimization and the related concepts and algorithms may play a significant role. In some situations one has differentiability of the cost function and of the constraints but the calculation of the exact discrete gradient is practically impossible due to the extreme complexity of the problem. In such situations, variants of Newton, quasi-Newton, and conjugate gradient methods not using exact derivatives may play an invaluable role; indeed numerical experiments have shown that they provide a substantial CPU speedup for some large control problems.

- Interface of Symbolic and Numerical Computation.

In recent years considerable interest has been generated in the area of symbolic computation for control. Although there is some research on combined symbolic and numerical computation, this area of research has a substantial potential for both academic research and engineering development. The interfacing of symbolic and numerical computing with computer graphics is a research area that could have direct impact on mathematical analysis, the development of CAD design tools, and even hardware capabilities.

- Parallel Algorithms.

During the past decade there have been tremendous technological breakthroughs in the area of vector and parallel computing devices. Although several branches of engineering and science have made use of this technology, the development of fast algorithms for control and identification remains in its infancy. Research into control algorithms to be implemented on specialized computer architectures offers an opportunity for the efficient solution of many classes of presently intractable distributed parameter and high-order problems, including real-time and on-line computational algorithms. Research in this area should be expanded and it should involve collaborative efforts of numerical analysts, computer scientists, and control theorists. In addition to standard numerical problems, new questions, such as the effect on overall numerical stability of problem decomposition and processor communication delays, have been raised that must be answered before practical parallel algorithms can be developed and understood.

Present development of massively parallel architectures offers important new possibilities for the field of stochastic dynamical systems, including stochastic control. The prototype of a massively parallel architecture is represented by the Connection Machine with over

64,000 processors. In the future there will be machines with several hundred thousands of processors operating in parallel. Massively parallel architectures are presently being experimented with in problems of image processing, pattern recognition, and numerical solution of partial differential equations. The simulation of random trajectories of stochastic dynamical systems is a perfect task for parallel architectures, since each realization of a random process can be calculated on a different processor, thereby allowing a fast computation of ensemble averages and other parameters of the probability distributions. These architectures may also permit the implementation in practice of theoretical results for the stochastic control of systems with partial information, such as the control of the Zakai stochastic partial differential equation.

Other research opportunities

This section contains descriptions of new opportunities in which the connections to the existing theory are not yet firmly established. However, the importance of these topics indicates that the appropriate mathematical developments of new control paradigms should occur.

- Control of Chaos.

There is currently vigorous research activity in the field of nonlinear dynamical systems, which is now beginning to have an impact on control science. Among some speculative ideas communicated to the Panel, two are interesting in this context: control in the vicinity of bifurcation points offers unique possibilities for using very small controls with large results, and steering towards a chaotic regime with a goal of replacing rattling noise (e.g., in mechanical systems) by a mix of incompatible frequencies that is less harmful to the system.

Chaotic dynamical systems have proven to be very useful for describing and quantifying a variety of complex phenomena such as chemical reaction dynamics, convection, and circuit dynamics. Sometimes it is desirable to control and enhance chaos rather than suppress it. For example, the formation of vertices in swirling flow is important in fuel mixing. The transport is directly related to chaotic particle paths ("Lagrangian turbulence"). The transport rate can be estimated analytically in terms of Melnikov-type integrals and by numerical simulations. If the system parameters (swirl rate, etc.) can be controlled, the system will respond accordingly. This suggests (i) that other control ideas (feedback, etc.) should be applied to chaotic systems and other features (power spectrum, Lyapunov exponents, etc.) may be controlled; and (ii) that the general theory of control should be developed for chaotic systems within the context of deterministic and stochastic dynamical systems.

- Computer-Aided Design of Control Systems.

Guided by control theory, control system design is a complex process involving engineering considerations and various trade-offs. Current interactive computer-aided design (CAD) packages simplify the design of control systems for chemical processes, rolling mills, and aircraft, among others. Making use of repeated system simulations together with parameter optimization, CAD depends critically on reliable and highly efficient numerical methods for both control simulation and optimization. In addition, computer graphics for displaying complex, often abstract information related to the design computations plays an essential role in the process. Research on both numerical and computer graphics methods intended for control design is needed. For example, simulation methods used in CAD must efficiently compute both system responses and their derivatives with respect to parameters. Numerical methods are needed to compute the boundaries of stability regions in parameter space. Optimization methods that need further computational development include non-smooth optimization algorithms that are robust with respect to design problem conditioning. Computer graphics research needs to address the problem of entering complex system configuration and visualizing computed responses as well as the geometry of various regions in the space of parameters. There is also a need for the development of knowledge bases that would assist the user in various design decisions. While progress on CAD methods for linear multivariable systems has been rapid, there is hardly any CAD software for control problems with nonlinear or PDE dynamics, and much fundamental research is needed to make advances in this area.

- Decentralized Control.

Recent advances in microelectronics and computer network technology have opened new possibilities for the control of systems that are geographically distributed over large distances and have a distinct "interconnection structure" (e.g., large power systems). This has stimulated a strong interest in distributed control algorithms whereby the computational load for solving a special problem is shared by several processors, while coordination is maintained by information exchange via communication links. There is an urgent need for research on combined problems of communication, computation, and control that recognizes the interplay of these traditional disciplines in decentralized control systems.

- Intelligent Control.

Control theory as it presently stands deals with well defined classes of problems, where physical variables to be controlled and the control objectives have an established mathematical description. While the precise mathematical techniques embodied in control and signal processing have enjoyed success, they suffer from an apparent difficulty in adapting to the complexities that characterize certain advanced applications. Future intelligent controllers will deal with situations which may involve deciding what to control and which control strategy should be used in the face of changes in the control environment. Moreover, control strategies for future "intelligent robots" or other "intelligent systems" will certainly involve decisions at various levels of abstraction. Instructions for the execution of high-level commands in such systems may involve symbol strings rather than traditional control signals. These considerations suggest that a new type of control science will have to be developed which will blend present control theory with the problematic of artificial intelligence, and with computer science in general. Such a theory must be concerned with developing and exploiting the structural representation of models at different levels of abstraction and must strive towards a mathematical modification of the concepts of learning, adaptation, and organization. While such goals have already been envisioned by Norbert Wiener, only the recent spectacular progress in computer technology has made these goals realistic.

- Discrete-Event and Hybrid Dynamical Systems.

The classes of systems traditionally studied in control theory have involved variables defined as real numbers, governed by differential or difference equations. There are many situations, however, in which such models are not appropriate. There are at least two other classes of dynamical systems that need mathematical characterization and the development of control theoretical results. These are (1) hybrid systems, in which variables involve both real numbers and logical or boolean variables, and (2) systems in which variables undergo changes only at asynchronous discrete instants of time, sometimes called discrete-event dynamical systems. Examples of (1) are robotic manipulators, reconfigurable systems, and systems with many failure modes, such as large power networks. Examples of (2) include computer communication networks and manufacturing systems. Each class of systems needs a theory that would be used for analysis and design.

The control of hybrid dynamical systems will require a theory for dealing with a mixture of continuous and discrete variables with higher-level language symbols. Appropriate symbolic representation methodologies for such systems must be investigated in order to develop concepts that will enable us to model systems including both present state-of-the-art controllers and future intelligent control supervisory devices. The latter should be able to deal with decisions about the choice of a suitable control objective and strategies in the face of changes in the configuration or control environment, and would employ high-level linguistics instruction rather than conventional control signals.

Discrete-event dynamical systems exist in many technological applications, but there are no models of discrete-event systems that are mathematically as concise or computationally as feasible as are differential equations for continuous variable dynamical systems. There is thus no agreement as to which is the best model, particularly for the purpose of control. Finite-state Markov chains, Petri nets, queuing networks, generalized semi-Markov processes, finite-state machines, communicating sequential processes, perturbation analysis, models based on temporal or modal logic, and discrete- event simulation have all been used with some success to model special classes of discrete-event dynamical systems. There has recently been considerable excitement and significant progress with a number of these models. However, a complete theory of discrete-event dynamical systems may require fundamentally new approaches, involving techniques from algebra, graph theory, discrete mathematics, computational mathematics, and combinatorics. More specifically, the following modeling questions should be answered: How does one formally specify and reason about discrete-event dynamical systems? In particular, for a given model, is it possible to find an algorithm which decides whether or not it satisfactorily models a given set of real-time specifications? What is the complexity of such a decision procedure? A typical example would be the validation of a complex simulation program, whether it represents a communication network or the air traffic control problem at a major regional center.

CHAPTER 4. VIGNETTES

In this Chapter a number of "vignettes" are presented, outlining the present status and trends in selected subfields of control theory. The research areas chosen are sufficiently broad to give a reasonable indication of trends in the field. Nonetheless, they must be regarded as representative rather than inclusive of promising research directions.

Deterministic finite-dimensional nonlinear systems

Control of nonlinear dynamical systems is an area that has seen some major theoretical developments in the last fifteen years. At the same time, it contains major unsolved mathematical problems, some of which relate to very practical application issues. In engineering practice, nonlinear control systems are omnipresent; however, most of them have been designed by using traditional linear regulation techniques. The situation is changing now because of the increasing availability of cheap computing power. More advanced mathematical techniques are beginning to find their way into applications and thus provide additional stimulus for research in this area.

The theory of nonlinear dynamical systems without control has attracted considerable interest in recent years. That theory and nonlinear control theory have common roots in the qualitative theory of nonlinear differential equations. Some issues, such as stability, nonlinear oscillations, bifurcations, and presence or absence of chaos, are as relevant in control systems as in uncontrolled dynamical systems, except that in control theory one can modify system properties or behavior. Key issues of control are, therefore, the extent to which modifications of system properties are possible and how to calculate them.

Before proceeding further, we make the following remarks:

- In some control-theoretic work, the emphasis is placed on the study of nonlinear discrete-time systems, which arise in the context of digital computer control. Most system-theoretic issues have their discrete-time versions, although some results are harder to prove in that context. Due to limited space, this description will be limited to continuous-time systems.

- Already during the 1950's and 1960's there was interest in the stability of nonlinear feedback systems. Many interesting mathematical results were obtained for systems in which the nonlinear feedback involved only one variable. Among those were the Popov stability criterion for systems with a nonlinearity allowed to be arbitrary within a sector, rigorous justifications of the "describing function" method, and Lyapunov function methods. Extensions of these results to systems with many nonlinear feedbacks are still open.

- During the period from 1963-1970, several papers appeared that made use of Lie algebraic techniques to study controllability of nonlinear differential equations. They paved the way to a systematic use of these techniques in other system-theoretic studies. The standard Euclidean vector space is not a suitable state space for a significant class of nonlinear control problems. For example, the orientation of a rigid body relative to some set of axes is described by a 3 x 3 orthogonal matrix, which satisfies a linear differential equation whose coefficient matrix contains the angular velocities. By embedding the problem in the framework of matrix groups and associated Lie algebras, it was possible to reduce some system-theoretic questions to questions about Lie algebras generated from coefficient matrices containing the description of the system. This led to results that were easily visualized and tested. These methods are based on differential geometry and the underlying assumption of smoothness of nonlinear functions entering the differential equations. They are presently predominant among those working in nonlinear control theory.

- Another group of methods is well suited to problems which lack smoothness. These are methods associated with differential inclusions and nonsmooth analysis discussed later in this chapter. Some recent results on controllability are close to those achievable via the Lie algebraic approach. Even though it is difficult to assess the full potential of this direction at this time, the current activity is very encouraging.

- In addition to differential equations and inclusions, there are other models of nonlinear control systems. Given a differential equation model, various functional series (e.g., Volterra) have been developed to describe locally the input-output relation. Conversely, in some cases a given functional series can be realized by a differential equation model. The interplay between these models is central in the understanding of the relationship between input-output behavior and "internal," or state-space representations.

Equivalence of linear and nonlinear systems

An issue that is of fundamental theoretical and practical importance which has also led to a major recent achievement of nonlinear system theory, is that of equivalence between certain nonlinear and linear systems. We describe both its engineering relevance and broader theoretical ramifications.

The research in question dealt with the exact linearization of certain nonlinear systems via feedback and state transformations. The very fact of the existence of such transformations is surprising. Conjectured in 1978, they were established in 1980, and further developed in later years, along with engineering applications. The transformation has been shown to exist for certain classes of systems that are smoothly nonlinear in state variables, but affine in control. It is essentially a nonlinear feedback combined with a simultaneous change of coordinates, i.e., local diffeomorphism, in the state and control spaces such that the transformed system is linear. Necessary and sufficient conditions involving Lie brackets are available to check this possibility of exact linearization. These conditions are stringent, but fortunately they are satisfied for certain real engineering systems such as appear when controlling robot arms, helicopter control, or chains of electrical motors. Furthermore, they are verifiable by numerical and symbolic computation. On the practical level, the transformation allows the design engineer to replace the nonlinear system model by an equivalent linear system, for which an extensive theory and design methodology exist.

On a conceptual level, the existence of such transformations leads to a fresh point of view on nonlinear systems. The transformation can be interpreted as the action of a feedback group (an element of which is determined by a choice of the feedback and the local diffeomorphism). A particular nonlinear system then becomes just an element of an orbit in the space of systems. The problem answered by feedback linearization is therefore as follows: when does the orbit of a given nonlinear system under the action of a feedback group, contain a linear system? Known examples show that a rich set of nonlinear systems of practical importance can be treated as elements in orbits of feedback groups containing linear systems. That similar transformations of a more general nature may exist is the subject of current work employing Cartan theory. A great deal of present research deals also with techniques of transformations along reference motions.

Alternatively, if one looks at a linear control system as a vector bundle over the state space with the control space as a fiber, the "linear equivalent" nonlinear systems can be obtained by local diffeomorphisms of the bundle. Moreover, the known classification of linear systems via canonical forms and Kronecker indices extends to those control-affine nonlinear systems that are "linear equivalent."

In recent years, the linearization of the input-output behavior for control affine systems was obtained with the help of the immersion technique. The conditions obtained this way are much less demanding than those linked to the linearization of the state-space dynamics, but may artificially introduce unobservability. On the level of analysis, it is important to note that linearization by diffeomorphism is a specific case of linearization by immersion, if adequate outputs are chosen.

Related to feedback linearization are recent results giving local nonlinear versions of the "geometric theory" of linear multivariable systems. For example, quite significant results were obtained recently on the problem of disturbance decoupling and noninteracting control for systems with many inputs and outputs. In the case of disturbance decoupling, existing conditions enable one to verify whether a given output can be made independent ("decoupled") from external disturbances. The input-output relation for systems with many inputs and outputs can be made diagonal. [An example where such problems arise in a natural way is the problem of spacecraft attitude control, in which one wants to control or stabilize the spacecraft attitude relative to three inertial axes by using three control variables representing thruster jets.] In both problems the conditions are expressed in terms of Lie algebraic information about the original system, and constitute analogs of known conditions of the linear theory which involve supremal controllability and invariant subspaces. Analogous progress has been made in the problem of system invertibility (i.e., recovering the control from state and output information).

The above theories are "local." Some progress has also been made toward understanding global topological and geometric obstructions. Analogous to feedback linearization, one may ask more generally the question of characterizing systems that can be made simpler in other ways. For example, a challenging question is that of finding conditions under a which a system is feedback equivalent to one whose dynamics are described by vector fields which generate a nilpotent Lie algebra. A particular case of this problem reduces to the following differential geometric problem: given a singular distribution on a manifold, decide whether it admits a basis consisting of vector

fields which generate a nilpotent algebra. Instead of feedback transformations, one may search for systems which approximate a given
system in a suitable sense, and which have again a simpler structure. Considerable progress has been achieved on the approximation
of Lie algebras of vector fields by algebras of vector fields on homoge-
neous spaces of nilpotent groups, and this process has been applied,
for instance, to the study of local controllability of the original system. This research makes contact with the study of combinatorial
properties of free Lie algebras, hypoellipticity of differential operators, recent work on estimates for fundamental solutions of parabolic
PDE's, and other areas outside of control theory.

Nonlinear controllability and observability

The study of *controllability, observability,* and *realization* is the
first step in understanding the structure of control systems. The first
of these properties deals with the analysis of the potential effect of
controls on state trajectories. For instance, one may ask, for a rigid
body subject to external torques, which configurations of angular position and momenta are achievable from a given starting configuration. The answer will of course depend on the precise system model,
which is in this instance specified by the moments of inertia of the
body as well as the directional components of the torque or torques
allowed. The second property, observability, deals with the possibility
of determining the system state from partial measurements. For the
rotating body, one may ask about recovering the complete configuration from knowledge of some of the angular positions and momenta,
and of the external torques being applied. Finally, the realization
problem is that of determining the actual model of the system from
the observed correlations between controls and measurements.

The answers to these questions are not just of academic interest.
Although real systems are designed to be easily controllable, difficulties occur in the event of equipment malfunction. For example, in
the spacecraft attitude control problem it is very important to know
whether the attitude is controllable if only two, or even one out of
three pairs of thrusters work.

The above fundamental system properties have been the subject of a concentrated research effort during the last 15 years or so.
This work benefited from previous mathematical knowledge, and conversely, it resulted in new "pure" mathematical problems being stated
and solved. For instance, the study of controllability required the development of new results on the integrability of singular distributions
on manifolds, while the study of observability involved the proof of
new theorems on quotients of manifolds under certain group actions.
By now there is a fairly satisfactory theory for continuous-time sys-

tems as well as for various classes of discrete-time systems. Especially for particular classes of systems, like bilinear ones in which the only possible nonlinearities are products of state and control variables, algorithmic methods have been developed to solve many systems problems. For instance, results on the realization theory of bilinear models have been used in the modeling and control of distillation columns and electrical power plants.

Many questions remain open in these areas. As an illustration, take those dealing with controllability of continuous-time analytic systems. Here one basic issue is that of determining when a given system is locally controllable about an equilibrium point. A large number of either necessary or sufficient conditions are known for local controllability. These conditions are higher order analogues of the requirement that the linearization of the system at the given equilibrium point be itself controllable, which is sufficient (implicit-mapping argument) but not necessary. Necessary and sufficient conditions are not yet known. The global version of this problem is basically that of determining the shape of the reachable set from a point. All known examples result in sets that admit stratifications into submanifolds of the ambient state-space manifold, but the theory can only predict this structure in a very small number of instances. Current research in this area is related to problems in logic and analytic function theory dealing with extensions of the class of subanalytic sets. For smooth but nonanalytic systems, even more basic controllability issues remain unresolved, many of them purely mathematical. For instance, the possibility of applying linear-quadratic optimal control techniques to regulate a system along reference trajectories depends on the answer to the following question, for the control-to-state mapping: what degree of smoothness of a mapping defined on an open subset of a Banach space will ensure that this mapping must be nonsingular at least at one point if it is known that its image contains an open set? This problem ought to be related to a weak version of an infinite-dimensional analogue of Sard's theorem.

Recent work on nonsmooth analysis led to quite unexpected connections between differential inclusions and controllability in problems that do not necessarily have smoothness properties. At the basis of these results is a new theorem on local invertibility of set-valued maps, which in particular subsumes the Liusternik inverse function theorem in Banach space. By embedding the nonlinear state equation in a differential inclusion, it was possible to obtain new sufficient (and sometimes necessary) conditions of local controllability stated in terms of closed convex cones which, roughly speaking, replace the derivatives.

Historically, transfer functions and transfer matrices were used first to analyze linear systems and a state-space approach came later. In nonlinear control theory the state-space approach dominates. However, developments in nonlinear realization theory and other areas in the 1970's and 1980's suggest that effective input-output descriptions may be used for nonlinear systems. Volterra noncommutative power series and causal operators are the appropriate tools, but their structure is not yet well understood. Their better understanding should provide a tool, the role of which may be analogous to the role of transfer matrices in linear system theory.

This hope is substantiated by results obtained in nonlinear realization theory. After understanding the uniqueness problem and minimality in the 1970's, results obtained in the 1980's show that existence conditions are roughly analogous to those of the linear case. One set of such conditions is analyticity of the input-output map and finiteness of its rank. These conditions can be stated in all three formulations, that is, Volterra series, power series, and causal operators.

Feedback design problems

Unlike the case of linear systems, the design of feedback for nonlinear systems still lacks a unified theory. This is particularly true for systems with many inputs and outputs. Design procedures that can simultaneously meet the requirements of stability, robustness, and good dynamical response, for a large class of problems, are not yet available. However, progress made in the last few years is encouraging. Recent research has led to a number of results relating to the existence of feedback controllers with varying degrees of smoothness. This research has ties with Lyapunov stability theory and with the classical theory of dynamical systems. Techniques from bifurcation theory and differential dynamics have been used successfully.

One promising approach to the design of a (locally) stabilizing feedback combines the elements of nonlinear geometric control theory with dynamical systems methods, such as the center manifold theorem and the LaSalle invariance principle. The idea, developed so far for control-affine smooth systems, is roughly as follows. By using certain Lie derivatives associated with the system, one attempts to find a smooth feedback that constrains the closed-loop dynamics to an invariant manifold corresponding to zero output. If the constrained dynamics are asymptotically stable, it is possible to construct nonlinear versions of classical controllers which will yield a desired closed-loop dynamics. In the critically stable case, an adaptation of the center manifold theory must be invoked to prove stability of the overall closed-loop system. In both cases, a crucial role is played by the existence of global changes of coordinates to a normal form that is reminiscent of the control-canonical form in the linear theory. A subsequent adjustment of design parameters may be used to rescale the center manifold parameters and to achieve boundedness of trajectories starting from a given region containing the equilibrium. At this point, the invariance principle may be used to obtain stability. Typically, feedback gains will tend to increase with the radius of the desired basin of attraction. These ideas have recently been extended to design feedback laws for tracking, disturbance rejection, and model matching.

One of the obstructions to applying existing nonlinear geometric theory is that many systems of interest contain inherent singularities. Theory of singularities together with the use of global differential geometric methods have been suggested as tools for solution of disturbance decoupling and noninteracting control in such cases.

Nonlinear optimal control

Many optimal control problems can be solved numerically using algorithms based on open-loop techniques derived from the Pontryagin maximum principle (optimal control algorithms are discussed later in this chapter.). The computational complexity of many such problems makes it essential to develop a good theoretical understanding of the form of the solutions. In particular, it is of interest to find classes of optimal control problems for which the calculations are reducible to a finite-dimensional optimization. Recent results on optimal control have established that there exists a rich interplay between the Lie bracket structure of a system and the qualitative properties of extremal controls. Delicate mathematical questions arise, leading to problems that combine analysis and geometry related to the study of the stratified differential equations that result from the maximum principle. These are discontinuous, and often multivalued but, for real analytic systems, the discontinuities and the multivaluedness tend to be confined to lower-dimensional "switching surfaces," in some stratification of the state space. The solutions of such equations can exhibit pathologies, to which numerical methods are very sensitive. While such irregular behavior cannot occur in many problems in satellite and robotics control, it is an open problem to find classes of systems for which it can be a priori ruled out.

Hamilton-Jacobi theory provides a link between open-loop and feedback approaches to deterministic optimal control. The key is a first-order partial differential equation, called the Hamilton-Jacobi-Bellman (or dynamic programming) equation. Solutions to this equation provide the value (or optimal cost) function and characterizations of optimal feedback control laws. The theory has recently taken a significant step forward with the introduction of the concept of viscosity solution which provides a precise sense in which a function which is not differentiable or even can be discontinuous can be said to solve the Hamilton-Jacobi-Bellman equation. This concept provides a convenient criterion to establish uniqueness of solutions and their stability under perturbations of the model.

An alternative, the regular synthesis approach, attempts to give sufficient conditions for optimality for a family of trajectories that satisfy the maximum principle. One can prove that, if such a family satisfies some technical requirements, then it is optimal. The problem is to find a set of conditions that is both reasonably general and usable. Using tools from the theory of real analytic stratifications, such theorems have been proved for limited classes of problems.

Work employing nonsmooth analysis has brought many contributions to the optimal control problem. In the 1970's, necessary conditions for systems that lack differentiability with respect to state in the state equations were obtained. [Sufficient conditions were obtained later.] Those conditions are not easy to use, and further work is needed to develop efficient computational methods based on these results. Recently, earlier results have been reformulated by using different versions of tangent cone, that plays a critical role in this approach, and by replacing a so-called "calmness" assumption by more natural hypotheses. These appear to have simplified the theory. Additional efforts are continuing to strengthen the maximum principle by using selection theorems for convex set-valued mappings and to tie the maximum principle to questions of controllability. In another vein, connections with the Hamilton-Jacobi-Bellman equation are being clarified, and it appears that further progress may be achieved by combining the ideas of nonsmooth analysis and viscosity solutions.

Dynamical systems issues

The concepts and methods of dynamical systems have had an impact on control issues. For example, work on bifurcation control (how to deal with control issues in the presence of bifurcation) has been a very interesting development. In this case one has available the concept of imperfection sensitivity which is useful for the study of the corruption of systems near the onset of a dynamical instability. Recent work on bifurcation in the presence of symmetry will also play an important role in this development. The relevance of other dynamical systems issues, such as chaotic dynamics, are discussed in Chapter 3.

In engineering applications, the question of exploiting special structures is important. For example, synthesis problems for electrical networks can be reduced to problems in which the state manifold is endowed with a pseudo-Riemannian metric and the vector fields describing the dynamics are gradients. Mechanical systems whose Lagrangian is quadratic in the velocities have special bracket properties; these properties allow a simplification of the form of the associated Lie algebras and have already proved useful in the study of the optimal control of robotic manipulators. For mechanical systems with symmetry (such as rigid bodies with internal rotors) one wants to take into account conservation of angular momentum and the special Poisson bracket structures on the associated reduced phase space. Certain mechanical problems involving control of interconnected rigid bodies can be formulated as Lie-Poisson systems with forcing. It is likely that dynamic models of robotic manipulators are amenable to such a formulation. The utility of this formalism lies in the natural way it describes certain controllability and stability questions.

Distributed parameter systems

The term "distributed parameter systems" is used in the control literature to describe dynamical systems governed by partial differential equations (PDE's), functional differential equations (FDE's), integrodifferential equations and integral equations, and abstract differential equations in Banach space. The common feature of these systems is the infinite dimension of the state space, which introduces new issues not present in the finite-dimensional context, including the effect of singular perturbations, the regularity of solutions, and the selection of finite-dimensional approximations suitable for numerical calculation.

Control problems involving distributed parameter systems arise in many areas of applications, including aerospace and chemical engineering, resource management, biomedical research, etc. In fact, a large number of real systems are best modeled as distributed parameter systems. In control practice they are nevertheless often modeled approximately by means of low-dimensional ordinary differential or difference equations. This has been adequate for many applications; and it has been necessary, since the control theory of distributed parameter systems is not yet sufficiently developed to be routinely used in control system design.

Currently, there is an increasing number of applications where distributed parameter features are crucial to the understanding of systems dynamics and solution of the control problem. At the same time, the theory and its computational implementations have recently made significant progress, bringing them closer to practice. For example, solving the problem of rapidly slewing an elastic beam without overshoot or oscillation requires laboratory experimentation with a physical model of a beam equipped with various sensors, and the capability of designing a control system including the choice of sensor location and the computation of a feedback controller for the elastic beam PDE model.

Historically, control theory for distributed parameter systems has to a large extent followed the research agenda defined by the state-space approach to finite-dimensional linear systems. Thus much attention has been focused on issues such as controllability, stabilization, and—for stochastic problems—versions of the Kalman filter and its associated operator Riccati equation. Beginning in the early sixties, methods of classical analysis were applied to study such questions as the Pontryagin maximum principle and the validity of the bang-bang principle in systems governed by wave or heat equations. The controllability of the wave equation using boundary controls, and assuming smooth initial data, was also established by what might be called "classical methods." More recently, other functional analytic tools have been used: the theory of strongly continuous semigroups, for example, to study operator Riccati equations and their finite-dimensional approximation; and the theory of boundary value problems for partial differential equations, for example, to treat infinite-dimensional analogues of the classical linear-quadratic regulator problem.

These theories have been profoundly affected by the development of PDE theory and new computational algorithms. This development has built a strong connection between the theory of boundary value problems for PDE's and control theory. Many control problems, mostly PDE versions of the linear-quadratic problem, were analyzed and general strategies for numerical approximations for this problem were developed. A conceptual framework for several classes of applied control problems formulated in terms of PDE's was provided, and exemplary solutions of industrial problems using this technique were shown. Among several applications of this approach we mention the design of the gas flow control system for the French national network of pipelines and the feedback control of flexible structures done at ICASE at NASA Langley.

Most theoretical work on the control of distributed parameter systems has concentrated on linear systems. Nonlinear problems are much more difficult and, with a few notable exceptions such as studies of certain bilinear systems, they remain a challenge for the future. There is a simple reason why nonlinear systems are so much more difficult: control theory, virtually by definition, is concerned with the presence of a variable control in the state equation. This control function has no a priori regularity, and indeed is often discontinuous even for finite-dimensional systems. In the context of partial differential equations one is thus forced to consider solutions with a low degree of regularity. Especially in the nonlinear case, the solution may depend discontinuously on the control, and may even fail to exist for an arbitrary choice of the control function. Thus the control of nonlinear partial differential equations is linked, in many cases, to the study of ill-posed problems.

In problems involving PDE's, an important question is whether the control and observation are distributed on the spatial domain, or concentrated. For physical and technical reasons, in some systems only the boundary of the spatial domain, or else some selected points in the interior, are accessible for external manipulation by actuators and for sensing. From the theoretical standpoint, boundary control problems pose much more difficult questions than those posed by distributed control problems. The difficulties manifest themselves in the fact that the shape and smoothness of the boundary play a role in the mathematical setup; also, problems in which the control acts only on a part of the boundary may arise. Finally, the operator mapping control into the state space is unbounded, and this can introduce mathematical difficulties.

The choice of the state space and regularity issues

The identification of a correct state space is the first step on which hinges the control theory apparatus in both its continuum aspects and in the numerical approximation. The choice of the state space depends in turn on the mathematical question of regularity of solutions, that is, on the degree of smoothness defined by the kind of state space in which these solutions lie and depend continuously on the initial conditions and the control. Only recently a regularity theory for hyperbolic systems and a few other systems has begun to emerge. The source of the difficulty is that, for boundary control and observation problems, the standard regularity theory based on trace theorems (which infer regularity of the function on the boundary from its regularity in the interior of the spatial domain) yields rather pessimistic results that would not guarantee regularity of the state in the case the control functions are not smooth (e.g., if the control functions belong to the space L_2 of square integrable functions). Recent work on control of hyperbolic equations has shown that, for problems with Dirichlet boundary conditions (i.e., when the function values are specified on the boundary), regularity is much stronger than that predicted by trace theorems, so that the state theory can be based on L_2 controls. In the case where only the normal derivative on the boundary is specified (Neumann boundary conditions), much remains to be done. In contrast to hyperbolic equations, the basic control theory for other linear PDE's, such as parabolic and diffusion systems, displays a higher degree of completeness. The question of a correct state space for delay systems has been settled for linear

FDE's of retarded type, where the product space $R^n \times L_2$ has been universally accepted (R^n is n-dimensional Euclidean space). However, for systems that are time-dependent, have delays depending on other variables, infinite delays, or delays in control, additional difficulties arise. The combination of PDE and delay equations gives rise to further difficult questions.

The issue of regularity may appear to be a mathematical nicety without practical implications. In fact, however, it is of great practical importance. Numerical methods for solving the regulator problem by using the Riccati equation depend in a crucial way on the regularity of solutions. If the latter is ignored, lack of convergence and incorrect computed solutions may occur.

Classical theory on boundary value problems for PDE's has not addressed problems with boundary data of low regularity, because such questions did not arise naturally in the classical context. Most theorems assumed the existence of classical solutions (e.g., two derivatives in the case of second order equations). Since discontinuous control functions arise naturally in control problems, control theory has posed the boundary value problems with low regularity of the data on the boundary, and has introduced a new way of thinking about them. And indeed, investigations of the exact controllability problem have not only emphasized the importance of the regularity issues but have also in some instances revealed new methods of attacking these problems. In addition, such research has led to new and unexpected uniqueness results for some classes of PDE's, significantly extending the classical Holmgren uniqueness theorem.

Stabilization and exact controllability

The questions of controllability and stabilization in infinite dimensional space are both mathematically intriguing and practically important. Physical examples of such problems can be easily found, e.g., active stabilization of flutter in aircraft wings is a critical technological issue; exact controllability of a deformable surface into a prescribed configuration is a problem of current active interest.

An important mathematical development in control theory is the solution of the exact controllability problem for hyperbolic dynamics, particularly with boundary control. There was a succession of results of increasing power and generality, applicable to linear dynamics, during the period 1972 through 1985. However, the applicability of the results was severely restricted by limitations in the techniques employed. In 1986 an important new tool (the *Hilbert Uniqueness Method*) was discovered which greatly expanded the range of problems that could be treated. In the past year, the exact controllability problem has been resolved for large classes of *linear* PDE's which model the dynamics of structural members of various types (such as elastic membranes, beams, and plates, subject to a variety of boundary conditions). It was soon discovered that uniformly stabilizing feedback controls for such models could be designed by similar methods. Work in this direction is continuing, as researchers attempt to apply the Hilbert Uniqueness Method to linear control problems in elastic shell theory, to viscoelastic and thermoelastic models of plates, and to other control problems in structural dynamics of practical interest which were previously inaccessible. In addition, an important recent discovery is that certain semi-linear perturbations of exactly controllable linear systems are also *globally* exactly controllable. Moreover, the same technique (which utilizes the Hilbert uniqueness method in conjunction with Leray-Schauder fixed-point theorem) demonstrates the local exact controllability of more severe nonlinear perturbations of exactly controllable linear systems. These latter findings represent the first general exact controllability results for nonlinear distributed parameter systems.

Exact controllability, uniform feedback stabilization, and optimal feedback stabilization design are closely related in the context of time-reversible hyperbolic dynamics. It has been known for a long time that once a uniform stabilizing feedback has been found, an exact controller could be constructed from it. On the other hand, optimal feedback design requires knowledge of the possibility of stabilizing the system for at least *one* feedback. Approximate controllability to the zero state does not answer this question, because the uncontrolled residual may in time destabilize the system. However, exact controllability means that all the modes can be steered to rest simultaneously. As a consequence, the linear-quadratic problem with an infinite time horizon has finite cost for at least one control, which implies the existence of an optimal control. Then concepts important in the design of the exact controller may be used to construct the optimal control as a feedback and to characterize the feedback operator.

Numerical methods for control and identification

Within the framework of distributed parameter systems, the operator Riccati equation is a generalization of the matrix Riccati equation. The general approach to computation of the Riccati operators consists of replacing the original system by a finite-dimensional approximation, then using available numerical methods for linear systems to solve matrix Riccati equations and increasing the dimension of the approximating system to increase accuracy. Convergence of these methods hinges on three crucial issues: convergence of the approximations for the original system, convergence of the approximation to the adjoint system, and uniform stabilizability of the approximating systems.

Convergence of approximation schemes from the point of view of open-loop control has been studied extensively for several classes of systems that can be described by semigroups of operators. The method most often used to show convergence is based on the Trotter-Kato approximation theorem for semigroups. This method has been applied successfully to establishing convergence for systems of functional differential equations for finite difference, spline, and spectral methods and later applied also to parabolic PDE's with both distributed and boundary control. Applications of such methods to hyperbolic systems in maximal regularity spaces are now being studied.

Preservation of uniform stabilizability and controllability under finite-dimensional approximation schemes is a crucial numerical issue brought out by control studies. Even a simple parabolic equation with boundary control that is controllable in an appropriate function space, may exhibit vanishing controllability of finite-dimensional approximations. Recently, it has been shown for certain classes of approximations for delay and parabolic equations that uniform stabilizability is closely related to the question of how closely the approximations reproduce the spectrum of the operator representing the autonomous part of the system. Preservation of both order of the method and "spectral consistency" was shown to be possible via careful construction of the approximating schemes. While there are more results on delay and parabolic equations, the case of hyperbolic systems with boundary control still represents a major challenge. One of the interesting points is the development of verifiable error estimates for various schemes, translated to the level of the Riccati operator.

An issue related to these numerical questions is parameter estimation in certain PDE's and delay equations via schemes that use the same type of approximations as in the context of control. Here, it has been shown that one can obtain convergent approximation schemes for several classes of systems, and they lend themselves well to various applications in both lightly damped structures and in various models employed in the life sciences. Several of these schemes have now been implemented on supercomputers.

Problems involving delays

The control of systems involving time delays poses special difficulties of both mathematical and practical character. Systems governed by linear FDE's can be analyzed by methods similar to those used in PDE's, but a lack of coercivity and other features create special difficulties. Nonlinear systems of even very low order can have complicated behavior. State-dependent delays, infinite delays, or systems described by Volterra integro-differential equations present various mathematical challenges. Such problems arise in aero-elasticity, visco-elasticity, in some resource management research, and in life sciences.

Feedback control theory exists for linear ordinary differential equations with delays. However, the nonlinear case is not well understood, and the optimal control questions arising in nonsmooth functional differential equations are very difficult.

PDE's with delay in observation and control also represent difficult mathematical challenges. A particularly interesting case arises when there is a delay in the feedback loop used for the boundary stabilization of the wave equation. Some dangerous pathologies have been discovered, such as loss of stability for "almost" arbitrary delays in certain otherwise stable boundary feedback schemes. This suggests that certain known boundary stabilization schemes may be not robust enough to tolerate delays introduced by a control microprocessor in the loop.

Robustness and perturbations

One problem that must be addressed for distributed parameter systems is that of dealing with the rather limited theory of perturbations. One basic difficulty is that hyperbolic operators change character under perturbations, and the theoretical framework valid for the unperturbed system may be invalid under perturbations. Furthermore, a system governed by partial differential equations may have perturbations in the spatial domain (domains with holes, irregular boundaries, etc.), singular perturbations on the operator, perturbations in the coefficients such as those arising in homogenization theory, and perturbation in a form of a delay, or perturbation in the value of the delay. It is not known what effects such perturbations might have on control laws and the fidelity of numerical simulations.

Dynamics and control of flexible or mixed structures

The dynamics and control of interconnected rigid and flexible structures such as robotic, aeronautic, and space structures, involve a number of issues of engineering and mathematical interest. These problems involve difficulties in modeling, in mathematical analysis, and in numerical implementation. First of all, the formulation of the basic dynamical models is a nontrivial step. In modeling rotating systems with continuum-mechanical components such as plates, shells, or beams, nonlinear models (e.g., the so-called geometrically exact models) display behavior which is in certain instances qualitatively quite different from what is observed in linear and semi-linearized models. For example, if one views a plate or beam equation of say Euler-Bernoulli type as an approximation of a geometrically exact model, then the processes of *attachment* to a rapidly rotating rigid body (think of helicopter blades) and *approximation* do not commute. Done in the wrong order, the procedure can lead to spurious softening and hence to completely erroneous results even for small deflections. Thus, proper attention to dynamic modeling is a first crucial step. This is probably important even for "robust" techniques—all too often practical problems are "fixed up" in unsatisfactory ad hoc ways to account for bad modeling. We give below an example of the sort of difficulty one encounters when modeling of satellites, such as Explorer I, is not carried out properly.

Another example of a modeling question is how to properly model composite and perforated materials. For example, with a truss-like system, should one use a homogenization procedure, and if so, how? How good a solution does such an approach give? If one knows how to control or stabilize the approximated system, how good and implementable is it for the real system? Such questions are just beginning to be attacked. It is known in other contexts that finite-dimensional approximations might lead to erroneous conclusions regarding the controllability of a partial differential equation—for example, a beam with endloading has this difficulty. One can view these questions in the broad framework of the issue of the commutativity of control and asymptotics. The examples of flexible and mixed structures will be a good testing ground for the needed mathematical development.

Before describing the broader control-theoretic problems related to these systems, it will be useful to obtain a refined understanding of the relevant nonlinear mechanics. Recent work on the asymptotic dynamics of structures with elastic beam attachments goes a long way toward characterizing the states of rotational equilibrium. These results point to a rather complex nonlinear relationship between the equilibrium shape of the beam and the corresponding (constant) equilibrium angular velocity. A deeper understanding of these relationships and the ways in which they depend on important mechanical parameters (elastic moduli, mass distribution, angular momentum, etc.) will provide an important foundation for research on the nonlinear control theory of complex rotating mechanical systems.

Recent developments in Hamiltonian dynamics and coupling of

systems with symmetries (such as invariance under Euclidean motions) has shed new light on some of these issues. Likewise, engineering questions have suggested new mathematical structures. This commonality leads to new and interesting applications of Hamiltonian methods such as the energy-Casimir method (for determining nonlinear stability) and bifurcation of Hamiltonian systems with symmetry (for uncovering nontrivial branches of new solutions when system parameters are varied) which should apply to space structures, for instance. Other tools borrowed from Hamiltonian systems theory have led to new results on periodic solutions of systems near equilibria, including information on their spatial symmetry, and to the proof of nonintegrability in certain regimes of phase space. These results also suggest how to construct numerical integration schemes that preserve energy and angular momentum, avoiding systematic biases or oscillations that can occur in other algorithms, even very accurate ones. When dissipation is added, all of these techniques appear to be naturally compatible with Lyapunov and invariance principle methods.

Control-theoretic techniques are important to develop in this mechanics context. It is an illustration of the general idea that it is useful to have control-theoretic ideas adapted to a specific context and use the special structure of that context. For example, one wants to exploit conservation of angular momentum in the control of lightweight flexible space structures and to further attack the problem using a combination of analytical, numerical, and experimental techniques in a coordinated fashion.

All of this development, which is still very much the subject of current research, indicates the vitality and usefulness of mathematical developments in a variety of areas to problems of interest to control theory. The interplay between theory, numerics, and engineering practice suggests new techniques that are of great benefit to each of the individual areas.

Some painful lessons were learned in the early days of the U.S. space exploration program that brought home the point that dynamic interactions between rigid and flexible components of a spacecraft are important. A famous example in this regard is the Explorer I mission in 1958. Energy dissipation in whip antennas attached to a passive spinning body caused instability and an end-over-end tumble. The key lesson here was that *passive spin stabilization about the minor axis, while feasible in rigid bodies, is not possible in the presence of dissipative flexible components.*

The experience with Explorer I and later experiences with missions such as the Orbiting Geophysical Observatory III in 1966 (in this case excessive oscillations were induced by control system interactions with flexible beams) led to a vigorous program of research in multibody systems with flexible components. The approximate analytic and numerical techniques developed in the course of this research were quite successful in suggesting good designs for spacecraft of modest size and flexibility.

A new generation of spacecraft with very large flexible components (radar arrays, solar collectors, truss structures) are presenting new challenges to our abilities to model and accurately predict the dynamic behavior of such structures in space. It is necessary to have the proper tools to do this since the requirements on the performance of these new spacecraft are quite unprecedented. The Hubble Space Telescope, to be launched in the near future, is expected to have a pointing accuracy of 0.01 arc sec on rms jitter less than 0.007 arc sec.

Refined mathematical models and analyses will be necessary to attack such problems with a degree of confidence. New control methodologies will be necessary to maintain the effects of dynamic interactions in such large space structures within prescribed limits.

Stochastic control

Realistic treatments of physical or organizational systems frequently involve environmental and modeling uncertainties. Stochastic control theory involves the study of recursive estimation and control of dynamical systems in which these uncertainties are explicitly modeled as random variables or stochastic processes. The uncertainties may arise, for example, as noise in communications devices, unknown system parameters (possibly time varying) or random arrival and processing rates in a queuing network.

Methods developed earlier, including Kalman filtering and minimum variance tracking control algorithms have found frequent use in such applications as aerospace guidance and control problems and in industrial batch processing. These techniques were based on linear system models. It has been a problem of long standing to find implementable algorithms for nonlinear recursive estimation and stochastic control. Moreover, several recent areas of application have generated challenging estimation and stochastic control problems. Among them are: signal processing and inverse problems of computer vision and medical imaging, routing and flow control in computer networks, electrical power generation and distribution, resource management, and investment. There is a need for stochastic recursive algorithms for decentralized and parallel processing and control, with loosely coupled processors at physically separated locations.

Markov diffusion processes and stochastic control

Markov models have the appealing property that the current state is a sufficient statistic for the future time evolution of the Markov process. Markov diffusion processes arise as solutions to stochastic differential equations driven by white-noise inputs. Through the method of diffusion approximation, they also arise as limits of non-Markov processes and of many-state Markov chains with nearest neighbor interactions. The diffusion approximation method is widely used, for example in communication theory, chemical physics, and queuing network analyses.

Dynamic programming is a common technique used to study optimal control of Markov processes. The dynamic programming principle leads not only to the description of an optimal feedback control policy, but also to deterministic equations or inequalities satisfied by the optimal cost function. For controlled Markov diffusions this leads to certain classes of nonlinear, second-order partial differential equations which obey a maximum principle. These equations may have no smooth solution satisfying the appropriate initial or boundary conditions. However, nonsmooth solutions exist, and are unique in the class of viscosity solutions. Indeed, the notion of "viscosity solution," a relatively recent concept, is the right notion of "weak solution" for these differential equations. Although the theory of viscosity solutions can be developed without the use of probabilistic methods, many results have simple proofs based on representing the solution as the value function of a stochastic control problem or differential game. This provides a significant role for stochastic control methods in the theory of nonlinear, second-order PDE's of elliptic or parabolic type. Viscosity solution methods also provide a convenient analytical technique for asymptotic problems in nonlinear PDE's and in the theory of large deviations for nearly deterministic Markov diffusions.

Nonlinear estimation

Intimately connected with stochastic control theory are questions of recursive statistical estimation, including filtering, detection, and system parameter identification. In many practical problems it is not possible to measure the system state variables exactly. Stochastic control with partial observations is thus inherently concerned with estimating the state from noisy or incomplete measurements. The widely used Kalman-Bucy filter solves a special case of this problem, in which the state dynamics and observations are linear and the disturbances are Gaussian. More recent work on nonlinear state estimation has been concerned with recursive algorithms for calculating either the entire conditional distribution of the state given past measurements, or else some particular estimate such as the conditional mean. Recursiveness is crucial: since observations are typically being received continuously, the estimate of the state must be continuously revised to take into account the new data. Such algorithms will require sophisticated hardware and software, including Monte Carlo techniques, symbolic calculations, parallelism, and VLSI. An important issue is the inclusion of realistic bounds and limits in the nonlinearities of the models: this will prohibit the use of many smoothness arguments that have been used in the theory so far. Above all, it remains to narrow the gap between existing theoretical results and the ad hoc estimation procedures actually used in current engineering practice.

Many of the ideas of estimation and stochastic control relate directly to signal processing, and many fundamental ideas in signal processing have come from "control"-oriented people. Algorithms for adaptive arrays and channel equalization are of the recursive type dealt with in control but often involve different statistical patterns or nonlinearities. Various problems in such areas as computer vision and remote sensing can profitably be viewed as problems of nonlinear state estimation for random fields. For Markov random field models, the method of maximum a posteriori probability leads to the problem of globally minimizing an associated energy function. A stochastic gradient algorithm, called simulated annealing, is among the techniques used for this purpose.

Other topics in stochastic control

Several important types of stochastic control problems are modelled in terms of discrete-event systems, in which the state changes only at discrete instants of time. Examples of such systems are computer/communication networks and production or assembly lines, where the time evolution of the system depends on discrete events such as the arrival or departure of a job, or the completion of a task or message process. Typical kinds of control actions involve scheduling of tasks, routing of messages, and dynamic resource allocation. One of the challenges to stochastic control theory is to develop a collection of methods appropriate for discrete-event problems. Queuing models are useful in some cases; in others, diffusion approximation methods can be applied to reduce a discrete-event problem to the control of a Markov diffusion. The limiting diffusion control problem is one of "singular" or "bounded variation" control in current terminology. The singular control formulation is flexible enough to include both traditional control of diffusions and impulsive control as well. As such, it promises to be a useful tool in future developments in stochastic control theory.

There are mathematically challenging research opportunities in the field of stochastic adaptive control, where the goal is twofold: to identify unknown system parameters recursively, and at the same time to control the system in an optimal fashion. Many of the known results depend on minimum contrast or maximum likelihood estimates, which are not easily computable. In addition, much of the work has involved complete (noiseless) state observations. Stochastic approximation-type algorithms seem particularly suited to the estimation of the parameters in such problems, and such algorithms are well suited to analysis by the so-called Ordinary Differential Equation (ODE) Method. That is, the convergence of the parameter estimation algorithm can often be analyzed by studying the stability of an "averaged" differential equation. Mathematically challenging problems arise in proving that, for each value of the unknown parameters, an augmented Markov process has a unique invariant measure; this sometimes involves interesting and difficult questions in ergodic theory and stochastic processes which cannot be solved by the application of standard results.

Another direction is the analysis of decentralized stochastic control systems. These are characterized by the presence of several decision makers, each having access to different information and making its own local decisions to further a global, system-wide goal. Such control systems are useful in cases where delays due to communication or computation render centralized control schemes impractical, or where fault-tolerance is important. Static team decision theory has been used to analyze decentralized control systems; however, techniques are only available for solving certain special classes of team problems. Challenging tasks for the future include the study of dynamic teams, and also other issues such as the determination of how much information should be shared and how much should be processed locally.

Problems of stochastic control involving diffusions or large Markov chains lead to difficult questions of numerical analysis. The difficulties are not likely to be solved simply by using larger computers, important though that may be. For large Markov chains, one must learn how to exploit special structures, and even how to impose special structures so as to get a good solution. Computational alternatives to the usual method of dynamic programming are needed, as are heuristic methods for aggregation and disaggregation. Variable structure or "multilevel" approximations are required for the numerical solution of diffusion problems. In many cases, successful computations will depend on a proper mix of analytical and Monte Carlo methods. In France, there is a pioneering effort at INRIA to develop "expert system" techniques for stochastic control and identification, discussed further in the section on computational methods.

Algebraic and geometric aspects of linear system theory

The *state-space* approach to linear control theory consists of the study of questions related to triples of real or complex matrices (A,B,C). These matrices represent the autonomous dynamics of the system, the influence of control actions, and the projection onto the measured or observed variables, respectively. The matrix A is square, B has as many rows as A, and C has as many columns as A. Linear algebra has provided the natural tools used in this context. Alternatively, linear systems can be studied in the *frequency domain*, where interest is restricted to the effect of controls on observations. This latter approach employs as a model the transfer matrix of the given system, a matrix of rational functions which is built from B, C, and the resolvent of A. Methods from complex variables are naturally used in this case. Since the early sixties an enormous amount of research has gone into the study of linear systems, both in the state-space and frequency framework, as well as regarding the relationships between the two approaches. This research has been successful to the point that a considerable number of computer-aided design packages are now available based on these theoretical developments, as documented in other parts of this report.

The field of (finite-dimensional, deterministic) linear system theory exhibits a continued vitality as new questions are posed regarding the possibilities and limitations of the various design techniques. This presents opportunities for researchers in various areas of mathematics. As an illustration, consider the problems related to the study of transfer matrices. This study originated with the frequency domain analysis of feedback amplifiers, and traditionally focused on the study of the poles and zeros of the relevant rational functions. A modern interpretation of the transfer function is in terms of curves in Grassmann manifolds, with system theoretic invariants such as the number of integrators needed to synthesize a system corresponding to the Chern class of certain projective bundles associated to such curves. As described below, this novel interpretation allowed for the successful application of tools from classical and modern algebraic geometry. The poles and zeros of the classical theory can be interpreted abstractly also in terms of certain modules over rings of polynomials and various local rings, and this has given rise to a number of questions in commutative algebra.

A natural step after the study of single systems is that of considering *parametrized families* of systems. Families appear naturally in certain application areas such as parameter-adaptive control, where not all system parameters are known at the time of control design and must be identified during system operation. A large effort has been devoted during the last few years to the understanding of families of systems. As an illustration, we now describe three directions of research along these lines. Other closely related research deals with the generalization of linear system theory to "multidimensional" problems as appear in image processing, where techniques from algebraic geometry and several complex variables are routinely employed.

Pole-shifting problems for families of systems

One of the basic problems in linear control is that of characterizing the possible similarity classes of A + BF, for fixed (A,B) and arbitrary F. This is motivated by the interpretation of F as a *feedback law* used to control the system. The *pole-shifting theorem* states that, under a technical condition known as *controllability* of the pair (A,B), it is possible to assign arbitrary characteristic polynomials to A + BF. This theorem is by now classical, and its present proof is relatively straightforward. The achievable similarity classes are characterized in terms of the degrees of possible invariant factors. The theory is closely related to Kronecker's study of invariants of pencils of matrices.

The classical results suggest searching for generalizations of the pole-shifting theorem to families of systems; in the various technical versions of this problem, the entries of the (now parametrized) feedback matrix F are required to belong to a suitable ring of functions. The search for topological and algebraic properties of the parametrization that allow for extensions of the pole-shifting theorem has turned out to depend on the solution of various problems in topological and algebraic K-theory. Interestingly, these very elementary questions about vector bundles (or projective modules) had not even been posed until motivated by the need to solve the corresponding control-theoretic problems. For instance, it is necessary to characterize rings for which basic submodules of projectives necessarily contain direct summands. In topological terms, one needs to understand for which base spaces it is true that singular (or "stratified") subdistributions of a vector bundle must contain subbundles. An almost complete characterization has been obtained during the last couple of years, after a series of papers written by a combination of control theorists, algebraists, and others. This research has in turn suggested a number of new questions in K-theory, which result when taking the stable (in the topological sense) version of the above problems; in system-theoretic terms, one wants to know how much "integral feedback" is required for control. From a computational point of view, research in families of systems has motivated a number of problems in computational algebra and complexity that are related to the general area of linear algebra over rings.

The geometry of families of systems

Changes of coordinates in state variables do not have any observable effect on input/output behavior. This suggests the study of the quotient space obtained when identifying systems (A,B,C) that differ from each other by a canonical action of the group GL(n), as well as the study of all linear systems in the frequency domain representation, subject to a natural degree condition. Besides their intrinsic mathematical interest, these problems are of fundamental importance in understanding the global behavior of identification and adaptive control algorithms, which can be interpreted as evolving in suitable moduli spaces.

Starting around the early 1970's substantial progress has been made in the understanding of the geometric and topological characteristics of these moduli spaces. For instance, one has now a complete characterization of the integral homology groups for complex-valued systems without outputs, as well as a description of the mod 2 cohomology ring of the class of all systems modulo GL(n), expressed in terms of explicit generators and relations. This work turns out to provide a generalization of the classical Schubert calculus for the Grassmanian. In the case of the frequency-domain approach, the corresponding cohomology is still imperfectly known, and is the subject of much current research. It turns out that there are nontrivial connections between the moduli problems of interest in linear control theory and similar questions that arise in Yang-Mills theory, and this has also attracted some attention lately.

Output feedback design by algebraic geometry methods

A basic problem for the control of linear systems is to describe possible effects of feedback on the natural frequencies of the system. Among the most widely used classical methods for feedback design for scalar input-scalar output linear systems are graphical tests such as the Nyquist criterion and the root-locus method, which describes the graph of the closed-loop poles as a function of output feedback gain. The development of root-locus methods for multi-input multi-output systems was widely appreciated to differ significantly from the scalar case. Its ultimate solutions, using techniques from the theory of algebraic functions and Riemann surfaces, was the first of several successful applications of algebraic geometry to outstanding problems in control theory. It won an open academic-industrial competition run by General Electric in 1979 for controller design for a turbine engine. Using the interpretation of the transfer function as an algebraic curve in a Grassmannian, and the Schubert calculus, new results on arbitrarily tuning system frequencies by output feedback were obtained, which remain state-of-the-art today. Other important developments were: pole assignment using dynamic output feedback, a multi-channel Nyquist criterion, the application of intersection theory to enumerate equilibrium solutions of nonlinear systems, such as the swing equations for an electric power system, and the use of geometric invariant theory to solve basic aspects of the parametrization problem for families of systems.

Variational problems and optimization

Many questions of optimal control can be formulated as constrained minimization problems in suitably chosen function spaces. The specific problems that arise from control applications have a somewhat special structure. Nevertheless, for tasks such as proving the existence of solutions or formulating necessary and sufficient conditions of optimality, control theory shares common ground with other mathematical theories of optimization, including the classical calculus of variations, nonsmooth analysis, and mathematical programming.

Variational theory

The study of variational principles has a rich mathematical history. Mathematical physics—including rigid body dynamics, elasticity, and quantum physics—has been a source of many such problems. Variational formulations are also a valuable tool for solving partial differential equations.

Two areas where control theory has had a fundamental impact are the study of *existence theory* and *optimality conditions*. Indeed, L.C. Young's generalized curves and Pontryagin's maximum principle were developed to address precisely those issues for problems involving functions of one variable—usually time—in control applications. Developing a similar theory for functions of several variables has proved more difficult: lower semicontinuity and relaxation of variational problems are a focus of much current activity. The study of conditions guaranteeing that minima are attained was spurred by applications to finite elasticity, where the physically correct energies are generally lower semicontinuous but never convex. More recently, the study of relaxation has gained impetus from applications to optimal design and phase transitions. One key lesson has emerged: it is dangerous to discretize a variational problem that has no solution. Calculations done this way are inevitably sensitive to the choice of discretization, and they converge at best to a possibly misleading local optimum. The pursuit of existence questions is thus seen not as a mathematical nicety, but as an essential process in establishing whether a problem is well-posed.

The study of optimality conditions for variational problems has led to notable innovations in analysis. The concept of *variational inequalities*, developed in connection with problems in mechanics (e.g., friction, free surfaces) and with the control of distributed parameter systems, has turned out to be an important tool for partial differential equations more generally. The phenomenon of *dual pairs* of variational problems, which largely escaped attention in previous theory, has emerged as a fundamental expression of optimality for problems of convex type. Questions that have arisen about measurable selections, integral functionals, and convexity have generated much new mathematics.

Current work in the calculus of variations includes many fresh and exciting applications. One example is the theory of *liquid crystals*, which leads to minimization of an energy functional defined on direction fields. Solutions can have isolated singularities, which are being studied by a blend of analytical and numerical methods. Techniques introduced for analyzing area-minimizing surfaces and harmonic mappings are playing key roles in this theory. Another new application is to boundary detection in *computer vision*. The goal is to locate boundary contours in a measured image, and to produce a "cartoon" of what lies within. This is achieved by minimizing a weighted sum of penalties, reflecting the length of the boundary, the grey-level variation of the "cartoon," and the discrepancy with the measured image.

Nonsmooth analysis

A characteristic feature of many problems of optimization is a lack of smoothness (continuous differentiability), which interferes with methodology based on ordinary calculus. In classical variational theory a troublespot is apparent already in the definition of the Legendre correspondence between Lagrangian and Hamiltonian functions, which in order to be rigorous globally within the confines of the standard implicit function theorem requires assumptions so severe as to preclude application of Hamiltonian theory to all but the simplest and nicest classes of problems. In optimal control, with its emphasis on inequality constraints, the difficulties are still greater. Even today there is no single satisfactory answer to questions such as the "right" generalized formulation of the Hamilton-Jacobi equation in a context of either deterministic or stochastic control. The rapidly developing area of H^∞ optimization within control theory affords another illustration of the inherent difficulties in the absence of ordinary derivatives.

The source of such nonsmoothness in optimization can be seen in the fact that when a new function is constructed from given ones by a process of maximizing or minimizing, it is unlikely to inherit any standard amount of differentiability, although one-sided first-order directional derivatives of special sorts may well exist. In geometric terms, the corresponding question is how to work with the boundary of a region defined by many—perhaps infinitely many—inequality constraints. In contrast to the traditional picture for regions of mathematical interest, there may be little hope of studying the boundary piece by piece, and there may not even be any way of knowing, without an expensive computation, which constraints are locally active or redundant. Out of such considerations there has grown a body of mathematical techniques which began as *convex analysis* and has widened into what is now referred to as *nonsmooth analysis*. Instead of the usual gradient mapping associated with a real-valued function, it defines a set-valued *subgradient* mapping, and allows the function itself to be extended-real-valued and not even continuous. Subgradients in this sense, along with other related notions of extended differentiation, have been used in particular to obtain more powerful results on optimality, and are also being applied to controllability.

Characteristic of this new kind of approach, with its focus on set-valued mappings and the like, is a thrust towards reformulating a number of basic problems. For example, where previously one was content with the study of an ordinary differential equation supplemented by control parameters, intensive efforts are being devoted to *differential inclusions*; these merely require that the time derivatives of the system states are to belong to a certain set which depends on the current value of the state. This set might be described by a family of inequality constraints or specified indirectly. Differential inclusion models can serve as alternate representations of control systems, or in the study of viability of trajectories.

Optimal design

In many design problems, one desires to choose the geometry or composition of a structure so as to optimize some feature of its behavior. An important class of such problems is that of shape optimization, where the control parameter is a free boundary determining the domain on which the equation of state—usually a partial differential equation of mathematical physics—is to be solved. Optimal design is now a component of many computer-aided design efforts, especially in the aerospace and automotive industries. A typical aircraft design application is to choose the airfoil shape so as to optimize some quantity related to drag and lift, subject to various design constraints. One approach is to represent the unknown boundary using finitely many parameters. The resulting finite-dimensional function may not be smooth, but its minimum can be sought using methods for nonsmooth optimization. Another approach uses computer codes based directly on optimality conditions. These efforts have depended, of course, on the availability of large-scale computing. They have been a joint effort of not only control theorists but also civil, aeronautical, and mechanical engineers, numerical analysts, and applied mathematicians—a fine example of how optimal control can unify diverse scientific endeavors.

In the course of work on optimal design it was realized that some structural optimization problems do not have classical solutions. For example, optimization of a variable thickness plate leads inevitably to a plate with stiffeners, and the optimal removal of material from a region can leave behind a truss-like continuum. This led to the consideration of "generalized designs"—the analogue for these distributed parameter systems of "generalized curves." Since these generalized designs arise from rapid changes in the local geometry or composition, they consist essentially of composite materials. The optimization of distributed parameter systems has thus been linked quite unexpectedly to a problem of classical physics: the relationship between the macroscopic properties of a composite material and the microscopic properties of its fine structure.

Robotics

Robotics is an amalgam of several subjects having their roots in engineering and computer science with problems suggested by psychology also playing a role. The mathematical content of the subject is already large and continues to expand. It involves, in addition to nonlinear problems in motion control, questions in path planning, computational geometry, and the optimal deployment of computer resources.

Central to the subject of robotic motion is the idea of a kinematic chain. This is an interconnection of rigid members via joints which are, in practical situations, single degree of freedom revolute interconnections. For a motor-driven kinematic chain to have the capability of positioning itself at a general point in its workspace with a general orientation, the kinematic chain must have at least six degrees of freedom and six motors. Because of the complexity and nonlinearity intrinsic to this problem systematic methods are indispensable.

A key problem in the implementation of conventional robotic controllers arises as follows. It is most natural to describe the path which one wants the robot to take in ordinary rectilinear coordinates with the orientation being described by pitch, yaw, and roll. On the other hand, it is the motor shift angular positions that can be controlled. This makes it necessary to invert the transformation mapping the motor shaft angular positions into the rectilinear path as a function of the desired path. This is the so-called *inverse kinematics* problem. In a typical situation it can be expressed as an algebraic mapping although the degree may be quite high. The solution of these equations must proceed in real-time as the robot moves and this represents a substantial drain on the resources of the computer control system. It is of interest to note that the connection between mechanisms and concrete problems in algebraic geometry which began to be developed in the last century by Kempe and Peaucellier is now continuing with robotics and motion planning giving it new impetus.

The computer vision problem represents another interesting challenge. In the context of contour recognition, it has been recently studied by free-boundary variational methods akin to those used in control theory. Further progress in this direction can be expected. For control theorists, the most challenging problem in robotics (perhaps unsolvable with present means) seems to be the problem of integration of vision and control, e.g., the problem of grasping an object by a robotic gripper using vision feedback to steer the gripper to the object. The path to be followed by the gripper would be automatically generated in real-time in a closed-loop fashion on the basis of picture interpretation. The combined computational difficulties of image processing and robot control may exceed present hardware capabilities.

In a more speculative vein, robotic instructions involving the execution of some "high-level" command such as "Pick up the disk" involves a whole new control paradigm. By analogy to conventional servomechanism theory, which maps a signal onto the output of a system, this calls for a symbol-to-system transducer which would process the symbol string, and, making use of a world model if necessary, come up with the signals needed to drive the system. Along with the inevitable trend towards the use of more and more microcomputers in control systems there is a growing range of uncertainty, especially with uncertainty of a qualitative, or large-grain, type. By studying examples of this type we may hope to extract a suitable general model.

In some highly constrained situations robots need to manipulate only rectilinear solids; in other situations they may be required to manipulate smooth objects such as pebbles and even cloth. In the latter situation it is important to formulate a theory of how one can initiate and maintain a stable grasp and design algorithms which will allow one to implement the theory using a computer. Attempts to solve this problem have produced arguments based on three-dimensional mechanics and geometry (Gaussian curvature, etc.) showing the necessity of using nonrigid manipulators, e.g., membranes, fluid supported membranes, etc. The variational theory associated with these models is now beginning to find use.

Because the control systems used by robots are always implemented on microprocessors, there is often the opportunity to adjust the control laws by making software changes. This, coupled with the variable-load situations in which robots work, has made it natural to investigate adaptive control in this setting. Algorithms which sense the load and set the feedback gains accordingly have been implemented in some industrial settings already but only on one or two axes. At present a full six axis implementation of an adaptive control system would probably be too computationally intensive but developments in computer hardware may make it feasible soon.

The development of computer control of robots is facilitated by such simplifying assumptions as the rigidity of joints and links, and decoupling of model equations due to the existence of large gear ratios. However, when these assumptions are not satisfied, the control problem becomes mathematically complicated. If the joints or links are lightweight, and thus flexible, the assumptions of rigid body dynamics no longer hold. The mathematical model of the system then includes both rigid body dynamics and elastic beam equations, and becomes similar to the one described in an earlier section. The control of such a robot is a formidable mathematical problem. The next step, i.e., the design of implementable computer control algorithm for this problem, is also believed to be a difficult one. The elimination of large gear ratios by the use of direct drive motors reduces the flexibility of joints, but complicates the modeling and control problem in another way, by introducing cross-coupling. Here, recent advances in decoupling of nonlinear multivariable control systems by a linearizing feedback may become important.

In the mail responses to the Panel's inquiry, there was a criticism of standard feedback control literature by one of the foremost mathematical experts on robotics. The point made was:

"The vast bulk of the theory is linear. Moreover, the control paradigms involved are generally linear also. But now this leaves the subject in the strange position of treating highly nonlinear physical systems (e.g., robots) being controlled by discrete combinatorial mechanisms (computers) using linear models. Surely a case of looking, not where the penny is lost, but where the street lamp shines! I may also say that the relevance of the many linearization schemes proposed for nonlinear systems is not clear to me, as these generally assume that precise system models are available as a starting point, and it is not clear what advantage this technique retains if one assumes that the best available model represents reality only approximately."

The model uncertainty problem in the robotic manipulation setting arises because the shape of the objects to be grasped may not be known precisely, or because the load cannot be exactly predicted, or else the objects to be manipulated may be delicate (e.g., automobile glass windows) requiring high precision of grasp. Addressing this problem in the context of nonlinear control is indeed beyond the currently available robust controller theory (e.g., H^∞) and poses a significant challenge for the immediate future.

H^∞-optimization for robust control

A fundamental requirement of feedback systems is to achieve stability and accomplish performance objectives not only for a single nominal model (of the controlled system), but also for a set of models covering expected uncertainties about the model parameters and perturbations. Controllers which have this property are called "robust." Their analysis and synthesis is a major engineering and mathematical challenge which is not completely solved to this day.

However, progress accomplished in this direction in the last decade has been quite spectacular in the way it combined a sophisticated mathematical theory with practical engineering design considerations. To give a bit of perspective, let us recall that the traditional approach to the design of feedback systems assumed precise knowledge of the plant's model, including statistical properties of disturbances. The Wiener-Hopf design method was equivalent to the minimization of a weighted L_2 norm of a certain Fourier transform called the error frequency response (the "return difference"). The use of frequency response was appealing to engineers.

The state-space approach introduced in the 1960's has revolutionized feedback design by putting it into the realm of matrix calculations rather than Fourier transform techniques. This paved the way for the use of numerical linear algebra (Lyapunov and Riccati matrix equations discussed below). However, the basic assumption that the plant's model is known remained in force.

Since the mid-1970's it has come to be recognized that the robust design problem in the face of model uncertainty needed a different approach. One approach is to revert to input-output (as opposed to state-space) models and to base the design on the minimization of a weighted sup-norm of the frequency response. In this way model uncertainties can be accounted for in the design. This idea has spread quickly and became known as H^∞-optimization.

Quite fortuitously, a major body of existing mathematics from classical function and operator theory turned out to be directly relevant to design problems involving infinity-norms. This includes such topics as Nevanlinna-Pick interpolation, commutant lifting and dilation theory, and factorization theory for matrix analytic functions. Much of this mathematics was refined and generalized to meet the engineering situation. It has produced complete solutions for finding stabilizing compensators to meet infinity-norm constraints for multivariable linear time-invariant finite-dimensional systems.

Within H^∞ theory, three alternative approaches have been developed. The first makes use of a generalization of the Beurling-Lax theorem to Krein spaces and results in a family of solutions to this problem. The computation of the optimal compensator involves mainly linear algebra. The second, makes use of a generalization of the Nevanlinna-Pick interpolation theory and requires a sequence of algebraic manipulations of complex matrices. Finally, a third and very elegant approach to this H^∞ minimization problem uses results of Adamjan, Arov, and Krein, to reduce the problem to that of producing the best Hankel norm approximation of an unstable operator by a stable one. This approach uses simple state-space solutions to Lyapunov equations arising from the characterization of transfer matrices that are unitary on the imaginary axis, thus again tying state-space computations with frequency domain designs.

The above-mentioned solutions to the H^∞ norm minimization of the weighted sensitivity function rely on a special parameterization of stabilizing controllers which renders all the closed-loop matrix transfer functions affine in the controller parameter and the response shaping problem a *convex* unconstrained minimization problem in H^∞.

The advantages of the H^∞ approach are several. For one thing, the robust controller problem has been given a coherent, solid theory. Second, in spite of the return to the input-output model, the method actually retains some of the key computational advantages of the state-space approach, and offers new computational possibilities. Third, the designer can exercise considerable control over the shape of the resulting frequency response. This makes the method appealing to engineers.

Initial examples of H^∞ solutions consisted solely of small numerical examples used to illustrate the theory. Now work has begun on using the theory for real-world problems including control of helicopters, unstable aerospace vehicles, and process controls. One of the most significant uses of the theory has been to quantify fundamental achievable performance limitations associated with specific plants.

An example is the forward swept wing X-29 aircraft whose feedback performance is severely limited by the presence of right-half-plane poles and zeros in its basic airframe transfer functions. While the consequences of such configurations (e.g., large sensitivities) are well understood today, they were recognized even five years ago only as anecdotes in theoretical engineering texts.

Today's improved understanding of fundamental limitations puts control engineers in a much stronger position to get the most out of a given plant, and perhaps more importantly, to exert greater influence on plant configurations in their early design stages. This payoff is already evident in such current aerospace vehicle designs such as the National Aerospace Plane and the Advanced Tactical Fighter. It will also influence configuration selections, actuator options, and sensor developments in various chemical process installations.

Theoretical generalizations of the infinity-norm optimization approach are under way. Some results have provided explicit solutions for some classes of systems with delays. Work has begun on developing such explicit solutions for other classes of distributed parameter systems (including multivariable systems with delays and systems modeled by partial differential equations). Extensions of the theory to non-linear systems are proceeding in several directions. One such direction is to analyze how to handle computationally generalized objective functions more complicated than the infinity-norm of an affine expression. A second direction is to gain a theoretical understanding of the advantages or lack thereof in using nonlinear compensators for various types of linear robust stabilization problems. In yet a third direction there has begun the development of new mathematical theories of nonlinear dilation and factorization to handle worst-case optimization problems for nonlinear systems in a direct way (completely analogous to what is done for the linear case).

Perhaps the most important area of generalization is concerned with the use of more general optimization criteria which can incorporate the structure of plant uncertainty and also the structure imposed by simultaneous stability robustness and performance robustness requirements. The current technology can find compensators which optimize worst-case stability robustness, or compensators which optimize worst-case nominal performance (performance in the absence of uncertainties), and even compensators which optimize a weighted tradeoff between these two. What are needed are compensators which optimize worst-case performance in the presence of specified (large) levels of uncertainty. Analysis of and development of algorithms for the complicated optimization problems needed to achieve simultaneous robust stability and robust performance has also been progressing; various of these algorithms use linear programming routines as well as more traditional general nonlinear methods such as steepest descent. As such optimization problems become more sophisticated and solution algorithms more involved, more emphasis must be placed on study of numerical robustness and computational efficiency of algorithms.

One approach toward solution of robust performance problems is based on so-called "structured singular values," used as a more general optimization criterion. Other research is directed toward finding alternate characterizations of sets of plants, sets of stabilizing compensators, and performance requirements which are amenable to computational synthesis methods such as semi-infinite optimization.

The standard infinity-norm minimization problem is an unconstrained optimization problem. However, control system design problems often involve infinity-norm constraints and hence require more powerful tools than the ones mentioned above. Semi-infinite optimization, which is a branch of nonsmooth optimization dealing with maximum functions, is a promising new tool for the solution of constrained optimal design problems. Its characteristic is that it accepts constraints on graphs of functions. Its mainstays are the von Neumann and Ky Fan minimax theorems, the theory of set-valued maps, and the theory of nonsmooth analysis which provides a calculus for locally Lipschitz functions, including extensions of the concepts of directional derivative, gradient, chain rule, and mean value theorem. The theory of semi-infinite optimization deals with optimality conditions and algorithm construction. In particular, it provides rules for the construction of search-direction-finding maps for functions which are the sum, integral, or maximum of other locally Lipschitz functions. These maps are used in algorithm construction.

A promising area of application for semi-infinite optimization is in the synthesis of finite-dimensional controllers for control systems with distributed plants, such as flexible structures. Controller parameterizations which render all closed-loop matrix transfer functions affine in H^∞ depend on coprime factorization of the plant transfer function. While factorization techniques were originally developed for rational transfer functions only, it turns out that there are large classes of control system synthesis problems involving plants described by partial differential equations to which these techniques can be extended. In conjunction with robustness and H^∞ approximation results, this fact opens up the possibility of designing finite-dimensional controllers for flexible structures that meet very complex performance requirements.

Major research issues in the area of optimal synthesis of control systems with uncertain plants are (i) the development of effective, tractable and identifiable characterizations of uncertainty, (ii) the development of problem and algorithm scaling techniques so as to achieve good computational conditioning, (iii) the development of algorithmic subprocedures and simulation techniques that exploit problem structure so as to improve computational efficiency, and, in the case of synthesis problems with partial differential equations, (iv) the development of approximation techniques which ensure that numerical semi-infinite optimization algorithms are stable, and the results they produce converge to solutions of the original problems.

At present, it appears that a certain interaction with computer science is desirable. Since synthesis problems can be very time-consuming, it will be important to devise an interactive computing environment capable of displaying complex information and enabling designers to make adjustments to problem and algorithm parameters in the course of an optimization.

Computational methods for control

Computation is an indispensable component of control. Computation is needed both for off-line functions such as simulation, analysis, and synthesis of control systems as well as for on-line functions associated with control system implementations in embedded processors. Mathematical research must continue to support both these uses of computation.

For off-line functions, computational mathematics has made major contributions over the last decade in providing efficient, reliable, portable tools (numerical algorithms and software) for all of the common linear control design procedures. These include things like linear equation solvers, Riccati equation solvers, frequency response calculators, etc. which work routinely and reliably on problems with state dimensions "in the hundreds." (This is true for general problems without special structure such as bandedness or symmetry. For the latter, of course, much larger problems are also routine.) Future design problems, however, involve models with dimensions "in the thousands." These arise in complex distributed systems such as large space structures or interconnected networks of power systems whose dynamics extend over wide frequency ranges or spatial domains and cannot readily be reduced to simpler low-dimensional form. Traditional design algorithms must therefore be extended in dimensional capability by at least an order of magnitude, with little or no sacrifice in reliability. Technological advances in microelectronics have made it possible to design and build economically computer systems capable of meeting the challenge of solving complex and large-order numerical and nonnumerical problems at extremely high rates of speed. Parallelism in both processors and communications among processors and memories holds the promise of major breakthroughs in computation for control.

For on-line functions, the computational issues are even more complex. Not only are the computational requirements for control getting more rigorous, but they must also be satisfied in real-time and with unprecedented levels of reliability, fault tolerance, and self-check. The validation and verification of software are all areas in need of mathematical support.

As documented in other sections of this report, computational issues are a consideration in most branches of current control research. Substantial issues remain in what might be called "traditional" problem areas, as well as challenging computational questions raised by such applications as robotics and computer-aided design. One traditional field in which considerable success has been achieved is in algorithms for filtering. Square-root filtering stands out as a remarkable example of a situation in which computational issues came to the fore as a limiting factor in a real situation. Specifically, much of the early research on square-root filtering was motivated by analyzing data produced by interplanetary probes (e.g., Mariner). Standard Kalman filters encountered numerical problems which were correctable only by fundamental advances in the numerics being employed. While significant progress has been made in robust computational techniques for linear filters, more research remains to be done, particularly for large-scale problems. Moreover, very difficult theoretical and computational problems remain in devising efficient and reliable algorithms for nonlinear filtering.

Basic issues in numerical computing

The basic issues which must be addressed in numerical computing in conventional computing environments include analyses of both the condition of the numerical problem being solved as well as the numerical stability of the algorithm being employed to solve it. Other key issues arise in addressing the important details of software implementation of an algorithm. Increasingly, design of algorithms, their numerical analysis, and their software implementation involves, in an intrinsic way, details of the particular underlying machine architecture on which the software is run.

Analysis of problem condition is generally a very mathematically involved process and is intimately connected with perturbation theory. Roughly speaking, we say that a problem is well-conditioned if small changes in the problem data cause only small changes in the solution. The condition of a variety of numerical problems, particularly in linear algebra, has been well-studied and analyzed, resulting in computable or estimable "condition numbers." Such is not the case for condition estimation for many of the most basic control problems and stands out as a topic of considerable research interest. As an example, we might cite the algebraic Riccati equation which is fundamental to linear-quadratic, state-space filtering and control. While effective algorithms for the solution of these matrix equations now exist, a complete understanding of the condition of even the simplest types of Riccati equations is still lacking. Accuracy of computed solutions can not be assessed or estimated until condition can be reliably determined.

Again, roughly speaking, an algorithm is said to be stable if it does not introduce any more sensitivity to the data than is inherent in the problem. Many algorithms of interest can be shown to be what is called backward stable. That is, it can be proved mathematically that what is computed by the algorithm is (or is near) the exact solution of a slightly perturbed original problem. This is then near the "true solution" if the problem is well-conditioned. Stability has been proved for very few algorithms in control and substantial research will be required in the future to remedy this situation for algorithms deemed of unquestioned relevance. A related research area involves the use of algorithms whose numerical stability is unknown or in doubt and yet whose role in control design procedures has become somehow entrenched.

Another issue to be addressed in the software implementation of control algorithms is that computations on digital computers are done in finite precision, finite range arithmetic. This raises new, difficult mathematical issues. The many versions of floating-point arithmetic systems for digital computers simply do not possess standard or recognizable mathematical structures. While the control community has become aware of the fact that control algorithms must be solved or implemented in finite arithmetic, this key implementation issue has not received sufficient attention.

Specialized architectures

There is intense interest throughout the scientific and engineering communities in the design of novel computer architectures and algorithms for coping with present and future computational problems. Many existing control algorithms can be restructured to exploit the power of parallel machines, but completely new algorithms will be invented to solve problems considered heretofore impractical or impossible. This will involve collaborative efforts of numerical analysts and control theorists.

A high degree of parallelism can be exploited algorithmically in many control problems. In the control of complex systems one can also make use of decomposition techniques and various methods of simplification (e.g., aggregation, perturbation methods, adaptive control) as well as simulation. Numerical motivations should have an impact on the development of specialized architectures for control. However, we have not yet seen an emphasis similar to that existing in other areas of scientific computing (e.g., Navier-Stokes equations).

Research into control algorithms implemented on specialized architectures offers an opportunity for efficient solution of many classes of presently intractable high-order problems, including many classes of real-time calculations. Research along these lines is still in its infancy. Nevertheless, some research into control algorithms (principally for off-line calculations) on parallel and vector machines, and on implementation of control algorithms on specialized VLSI chips and systolic arrays has begun. (Such architectures are generally more conducive to implementing algorithms for signal processing rather than control because the high degree of regularity that characterizes many signal processing tasks makes them ideal for VLSI or systolic implementation.)

Little is known about parallel algorithms for control nor how to most effectively exploit concurrent processing and vector processing. For example, when a large problem is distributed among various processors, difficult questions arise concerning the condition of the resulting subproblems or intermediate problems created as a result of the decomposition. Similarly, the effect on overall numerical stability resulting from problem decomposition is a largely unexplored area.

Software

Software provides the primary vehicle for reliable technology transfer. It acts as the interface between mathematical control theory and its implementation for the control of real physical systems. The recognition of the important role played by reliable and robust implementation of control algorithms in (mathematical) software has been a major advance in the field.

There exist numerous challenging new areas for research at the interface between control theory and computer science. Many of these research problems are highly mathematical, ranging from numerical analysis to data bases and their representations to evolving paradigms for describing control problems at a higher level such as state transition nets, Petri nets, and the like. Much progress has been made recently in enhancing the productivity of control engineers and researchers by providing them with state-of-the-art control software and packages for both classical control and modern, state-space-based control. But a continuing problem which remains lies in increasing the awareness of the control community of available algorithms and software.

Theoretically, there are no upper limits on the size of realistic present-day problems that can be solved with current control design software. Most of the algorithms that have been developed for state-space models are for modest-sized problems (of dimensions no more than a few hundred) for which there are rather natural limits on problem size. However, there has been virtually nothing done for models with large, sparse matrices and this remains a most pressing algorithmic and software research area. Sparse matrices of the order of many hundreds or thousands are not at all unusual in, for example, models for the control of large structures. In fact, the integration of control with, for example, structures, optics, materials, and so forth is an obviously important and accelerating research trend. Such integration at the software level will eventually lead to metapackages that aid in total system design.

Symbolic computation in control problems

In recent years research has started on solving complicated control problems by using combined symbolic and numerical computation, followed by a graphical display of results. This area has substantial potential for both academic research and engineering development as a design tool. Known efforts have focused on nonlinear filtering and optimal stochastic control. In addition, there are continuing efforts to develop expert design systems for intelligent control systems in which the interface of numerical and symbolic computation plays a big role.

The nonlinear filtering problem has been attacked from the following angle. The problem of estimating a Markov diffusion process from observations is formulated in terms of stochastic partial differential equations for the unnormalized conditional density. By using the technique of asymptotic analysis to expand the conditional density in power series of a small parameter, one obtains a sequence of stochastic PDE's that can be solved in terms of Gaussian densities, but the complexity of manipulations increases very fast. By using Lie theory one can obtain a finite-dimensional Lie algebra for which the basis elements can be computed symbolically and then substituted into the equations defining the conditional density, leading to the computation of the approximate conditional mean that can be solved numerically. In somewhat related work, new connections were recently found between fast computation of Lie brackets of vector fields and such structures as Hopf algebras. These results were motivated by control theory, and should prove useful to control implementation.

The stochastic control problem has been studied in the context of an expert system that includes the following parts: automatic choice of an algorithm, check of well-posedness, automatic generation of a numerical routine, test of this routine on a numerical example, and automatic generation of graphic pictures of the solution. The system computes the terms entering the Hamilton-Jacobi-Bellman equation, generates a discretized version of the equation, and solves it numerically. Other available methods include a stochastic gradient algorithm and a feedback optimizing method based on decoupling. The system is written in LISP, MACSYMA, and Prolog, with Fortran to do numerical calculations. It has been applied to study problems arising in the control of an interconnected power system.

The interface of numerical and symbolic computation is an area where there are interesting research problems, and research in this direction will undoubtedly accelerate with progress in hardware capabilities.

Optimal control algorithms

The need for optimal control algorithms (for nonlinear as well as linear problems) began to be felt in the 1960's with the advent of the space program, where algorithms were needed for the computation of optimal rocket trajectories. Since then, the use of optimal control algorithms has spread to the solution of a variety of aerospace problems, economic planning problems, shape design problems, and, more recently, to the computation of slewing motions for large space structures and mechanisms with flexible arms.

Optimal control problems are among the most difficult of optimization problems: the decision vector is a measurable function, equality constraints are in terms of ordinary or partial differential equations and various boundary conditions, while inequality constraints may involve boundary conditions, entire trajectories, and controls.

With very few exceptions, optimal control algorithms for open-loop control in nonlinear problems have been obtained by formal extension of either nonlinear programming algorithms (which solve optimization problems with a finite-dimensional decision vector and a finite number of equality and inequality constraints) or semi-infinite programming algorithms (which solve optimization problems with a finite-dimensional decision vector and an infinite number of inequality constraints). Thus, there are optimal control analogs of Newton's method, the method of steepest descent, conjugate gradient methods, methods of feasible directions, etc. Since bounded sequences of measurable controls need not have accumulation points, the convergence of optimal control algorithms is analyzed either by embedding controls in the space of relaxed controls (probability measures) or in terms of special optimality conditions which characterize minimizing sequences.

Although current optimization algorithm theory makes the extension of nonlinear and semi-infinite programming algorithms to so-called conceptual optimal control algorithms relatively straightforward, the construction of efficient, computer-implementable algorithms for optimal control remains a considerable challenge. Conceptual optimal control algorithms are specified in terms of operations which cannot be carried out on a digital computer. For example, they involve the exact solution of partial or ordinary differential equations and the computation of search directions which require an infinite number of iterations of a complex search direction subprocedure. Implementation can be carried out in two ways.

The first is to decompose the original problem into a sequence of discretized problems and to establish rules for moving from one of the discretized problems to the next one, after only a finite number of iterations. The major theoretical issue is to ensure that the discretization and problem transition rules are compatible with the construction of a sequence which converges to a stationary point of the original problem. The major computational issue is to ensure that the computational effort in reducing the initial error by a desired factor is accomplished in a minimum of computer time.

The second approach to implementation does not require predetermined discretization. Instead, implementable approximations to the algorithmic subprocedures are constructed and the precision of approximation is increased as a stationary point is approached, either on the basis of tests or in an a priori predetermined manner. This approach has the advantage over discretization that implicit, variable step-length schemes can be used for integrating the differential equations of the system dynamics. Again, the major issues are convergence and computational efficiency.

As long as there are no control or state-space or shape constraints present, the construction of efficient, implementable optimal control algorithms is relatively easy. However, control, state-space and shape constraints tend to lead to optimal control algorithm implementations with search direction and step size computation subprocedures of enormous computational complexity. The resolution of this difficulty will involve the invention of simulation techniques which are specifically designed to take advantage of the fact that the iterations of an optimal control algorithm generate large numbers of neighboring trajectories. The invention of new search direction subprocedures, as well as novel, highly efficient algorithm implementation schemes, will also be required.

A useful tool for the analysis of convex optimal control problem discretizations is epiconvergence theory. Epiconvergence is the weakest concept (for variational problems) under which the convergence and rate of convergence of solutions of approximating problems (as defined by finite elements, say) to solutions of the original problem can properly be established. To be useful in the development of techniques for the discretization of nonconvex optimal control problems, epiconvergence theory will need to be extended to include results on the convergence of local minima as well as other stationary points.

Optimal control and mathematical programming

Although applications to problems in engineering have so far been the driving force in the development of optimal control, other kinds of applications such as to economics, resource management, and operations research have also attracted attention. An important mathematical project must be the adaptation of existing methodology to the needs to these other applications. For example, the notion of a control region that depends on the current state of the system (a sort of partial feedback) is essential in economic modeling but hardly ever seen in the control literature, much less addressed in the needed manner. Questions of convexity and duality, too, ought to be explored in many directions in order to take full advantage of properties that are often crucial outside the engineering realm.

The modeling of finite-dimensional decision processes in time has gone on in mathematical programming as well as in optimal control, but differently. In order to cope with the large-scale nature of the problems that arise and still be able to compute solutions effectively, mathematical programmers have placed heavy emphasis on linear dynamics and constraints as represented in terms of large, sparse matrices with a staircase structure. Linearized and discretized versions of control dynamics can also be represented in such a way. On the other hand, optimality conditions for problems involving staircase matrices can be written in a form that resembles the maximum principle in optimal control. There does not seem to have been enough thinking to date about the connections between these two approaches and what the different optimization communities can learn from each other. Perhaps the introduction of new problem models of a piecewise linear-quadratic nature could serve as a bridge.

Recent years have seen the rise of stochastic programming as a branch of finite-dimensional optimization in time, where resource decisions are made in the presence of uncertainty and in response to observations. The capabilities of modern computers are making it possible for the first time to calculate solutions to such problems. Fresh ideas in this area could well lead to new developments in stochastic optimal control, which has long been daunted by computational difficulties.

Adaptive control

Adaptive control is necessary in many applications, because the parameters in a system model undergo significant changes or cannot be measured with sufficient accuracy, rendering the application of classical feedback either unreliable or impossible. Reasons for this include the effects of changes in altitude or air speed of high performance aircraft, the inability to determine system response at high frequencies, or the use of low-dimensional approximations for complex high-dimensional systems. In some systems, the suppression of nonlinear or elastic components may lead to simplified models that exhibit large errors in certain ranges of conditions. Adaptive control attempts to address those problems by changing the parameters of the feedback.

Historically, early adaptive algorithms employed heuristic models in classical control such as the Ziegler-Nichols rules and elementary experiments on the system to tune the parameters of a standard three term controller. In the mid-seventies, some important advances were made, along two main approaches.

The first consists of combining an identification scheme to track the changing values of system parameters and a control scheme designed as if the parameters were known and time-invariant. The difficulty with this approach, called "self-tuning," is in the simultaneous presence of identification and control in the same feedback loop. It may be impossible to identify system parameters while changing the parameters of the controller. However, it was shown in 1973 that the optimal control can often be obtained in the limit, even if the identification is not accurate. This was followed by a considerable number of applications that confirmed the validity of this approach. Today, there are several adaptive controllers commercially produced in the United States and in Europe, especially in Sweden, which use modifications of "minimum variance" control.

The second approach consists of adjusting the parameters of the controller so as to make the behavior of the controlled system match closely that of a chosen reference model. This is called "model reference adaptive control." The system is assumed to be deterministic. Stability analysis methods such as those based on the use of Lyapunov functions are a primary tool for showing the stability of the adaptive control system.

Self-tuning and model reference adaptive control apply primarily to linear systems. For nonlinear systems specialized adaptive control algorithms exist. A prime example is adaptive control of manipulator robots, where the parameters change with mass, shape, and orientation of objects being handled. An important property of such systems is that the unknown parameters enter linearly in the nonlinear system equations. By using an approach that resembles self-tuning, stable controllers have been designed.

The need to apply adaptive methods to high performance systems has continually been a source for the investigation of alternative, more powerful adaptive control strategies. The goals of adaptive control are still far from being realized and there is a widespread agreement that the field is still very much in its infancy. Much of the literature consists of the design and analysis of particular algorithms. The notion of robustness, together with the now stated goals of adaptively controlling distributed parameter systems such as combustion and flow control, will undoubtedly broaden the field of adaptive control. One can anticipate that the next generation of adaptive control results will be based on methods from nonlinear dynamical systems and functional analysis. One can also expect that the development of a fundamental, algorithm-independent approach to some of the basic issues in adaptive control will take place.